OFFICIAL
SQA
PAST
PAPERS
WITH ANSWERS

INTERMEDIATE 2

CHEMISTRY
2007-2011

Publisher's Note

We are delighted to bring you the 2011 Past Papers and you will see that we have changed the format from previous editions. As part of our environmental awareness strategy, we have attempted to make these new editions as sustainable as possible.

To do this, we have printed on white paper and bound the answer sections into the book. This not only allows us to use significantly less paper but we are also, for the first time, able to source all the materials from sustainable sources.

We hope you like the new editions and by purchasing this product, you are not only supporting an independent Scottish publishing company but you are also, in the International Year of Forests, not contributing to the destruction of the world's forests.

Thank you for your support and please see the following websites for more information to support the above statement –

www.fsc-uk.org

www.loveforests.com

© Scottish Qualifications Authority
All rights reserved. Copying prohibited. No part of this publication may be reproduced, stored in a retrieval system, or transmitted in any form or by any means, electronic, mechanical, photocopying, recording or otherwise.

First exam published in 2007.
Published by Bright Red Publishing Ltd, 6 Stafford Street, Edinburgh EH3 7AU
tel: 0131 220 5804 fax: 0131 220 6710 info@brightredpublishing.co.uk www.brightredpublishing.co.uk

ISBN 978-1-84948-195-3

A CIP Catalogue record for this book is available from the British Library.

Bright Red Publishing is grateful to the copyright holders, as credited on the final page of the Question Section, for permission to use their material. Every effort has been made to trace the copyright holders and to obtain their permission for the use of copyright material. Bright Red Publishing will be happy to receive information allowing us to rectify any error or omission in future editions.

INTERMEDIATE 2

2007

[BLANK PAGE]

FOR OFFICIAL USE

Section B   Total
Marks

X012/201

NATIONAL
QUALIFICATIONS
2007

TUESDAY, 29 MAY
9.00 AM – 11.00 AM

CHEMISTRY
INTERMEDIATE 2

Fill in these boxes and read what is printed below.

Full name of centre

Town

Forename(s)

Surname

Date of birth
Day Month Year

Scottish candidate number

Number of seat

Necessary data will be found in the Chemistry Data Booklet for Standard Grade and Intermediate 2.

Section A — Questions 1—30 (30 marks)

Instructions for completion of **Section A** are given on page two.

For this section of the examination you must use an **HB pencil**.

Section B (50 marks)

All questions should be attempted.

The questions may be answered in any order but all answers are to be written in the spaces provided in this answer book, **and must be written clearly and legibly in ink**.

Rough work, if any should be necessary, should be written in this book, and then scored through when the fair copy has been written. If further space is required, a supplementary sheet for rough work may be obtained from the invigilator.

Additional space for answers will be found at the end of the book. If further space is required, supplementary sheets may be obtained from the invigilator and should be inserted inside the **front** cover of this booklet.

Before leaving the examination room you must give this book to the invigilator. If you do not, you may lose all the marks for this paper.

SCOTTISH
QUALIFICATIONS
AUTHORITY

Read carefully

1 Check that the answer sheet provided is for **Chemistry Intermediate 2 (Section A)**.

2 For this section of the examination you must use an **HB pencil** and, where necessary, an eraser.

3 Check that the answer sheet you have been given has **your name**, **date of birth**, **SCN** (Scottish Candidate Number) and **Centre Name** printed on it.

   Do not change any of these details.

4 If any of this information is wrong, tell the Invigilator immediately.

5 If this information is correct, **print** your name and seat number in the boxes provided.

6 The answer to each question is **either** A, B, C or D. Decide what your answer is, then, using your pencil, put a horizontal line in the space provided (see sample question below).

7 There is **only one correct** answer to each question.

8 Any rough working should be done on the question paper or the rough working sheet, **not** on your answer sheet.

9 At the end of the exam, put the **answer sheet for Section A inside the front cover of this answer book**.

Sample Question

To show that the ink in a ball-pen consists of a mixture of dyes, the method of separation would be

   A chromatography

   B fractional distillation

   C fractional crystallisation

   D filtration.

The correct answer is **A**—chromatography. The answer **A** has been clearly marked in **pencil** with a horizontal line (see below).

Changing an answer

If you decide to change your answer, carefully erase your first answer and using your pencil, fill in the answer you want. The answer below has been changed to **D**.

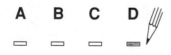

SECTION A

1. Which of the following elements has similar chemical properties to argon?

   A   Fluorine

   B   Krypton

   C   Potassium

   D   Zinc

2.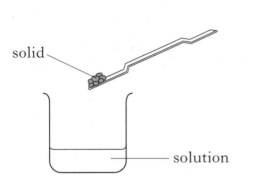

   Which of the following would **not** be evidence of a chemical reaction when the solid is added to the solution?

   A   A colour change

   B   A gas being given off

   C   The temperature rising

   D   The solid disappearing

3. Which line in the table shows the approximate percentage composition of air?

	Nitrogen	Oxygen	Carbon dioxide	Noble gases
A	78	21	0·03	1
B	21	78	1	0·03
C	1	21	78	0·03
D	0·03	78	1	21

4. Isotopes of the same element have identical

   A   nuclei

   B   mass numbers

   C   numbers of neutrons

   D   numbers of protons.

5. Vinegar is prepared by dissolving ethanoic acid in water.

   Which line in the table identifies the solute, solvent and solution?

	Solute	Solvent	Solution
A	water	ethanoic acid	vinegar
B	water	vinegar	ethanoic acid
C	ethanoic acid	water	vinegar
D	vinegar	water	ethanoic acid

6. Which of the following diagrams could be used to represent the structure of a covalent network compound?

   A

   B

   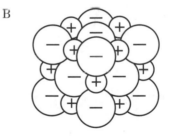

   C

   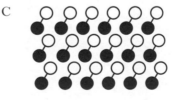

   D

   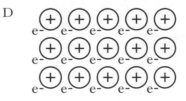

[Turn over

7. The table shows the colours of some ionic compounds in solution.

Compound	Colour
potassium chloride	colourless
potassium chromate	yellow
copper chromate	green
copper sulphate	blue

The colour of the chromate ion is

A   colourless

B   yellow

C   green

D   blue.

8. Gasoline produced by the fractional distillation of crude oil has a low viscosity.

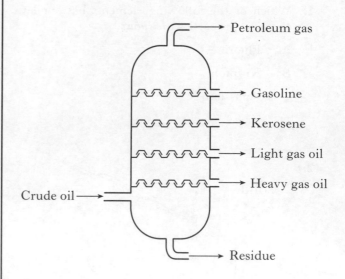

Which of the following properties also applies to gasoline?

A   High boiling point and high flammability

B   Low boiling point and high flammability

C   High boiling point and low flammability

D   Low boiling point and low flammability

9. The first three members of the alkyne homologous series are:

$$H-C\equiv C-H \qquad H-C\equiv C-\underset{\displaystyle\overset{\textstyle|}{H}}{\overset{\textstyle H}{\overset{\textstyle|}{C}}}-H \qquad H-C\equiv C-\underset{\displaystyle\overset{\textstyle|}{H}}{\overset{\textstyle H}{\overset{\textstyle|}{C}}}-\underset{\displaystyle\overset{\textstyle|}{H}}{\overset{\textstyle H}{\overset{\textstyle|}{C}}}-H$$

What is the general formula for this homologous series?

A C_nH_n

B C_nH_{n+1}

C C_nH_{n+2}

D C_nH_{2n-2}

10.

```
        H   H   H   H
        |   |   |   |
    H — C — C — C — C — H
        |   |   |   |
        H   H   OH  H
```

Which of the following compounds is an isomer of the one above?

A
```
        H   H   H
        |   |   |
    H — C — C — C — H
        |   |   |
        H   H   OH
```

B
```
                H
                |
            H — C — H
        H   H   |        H
        |   |   |        |
    H — C — C — C ———— C — H
        |   |   |        |
        H   H   OH       H
```

C
```
        H   OH  H   H
        |   |   |   |
    H — C — C — C — C — H
        |   |   |   |
        H   H   H   H
```

D
```
        H   H   H   H
        |   |   |   |
    H — C — C — C — C — H
        |   |   |   |
        H   H   H   OH
```

11. Which of the following represents an ester?

A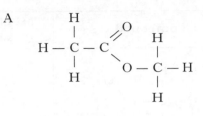

B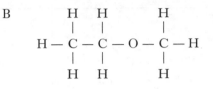

C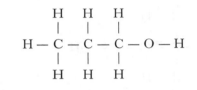

D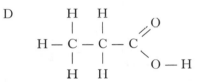

[Turn over

12. A student tested some compounds. The results are given in the table.

Compound	**pH of aqueous solution**	**Effect on bromine solution**
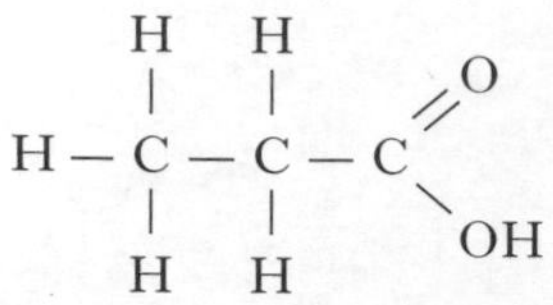	4	no effect
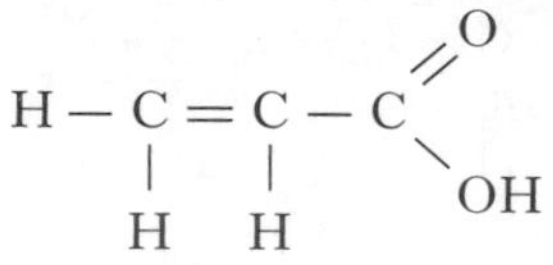	4	decolourised
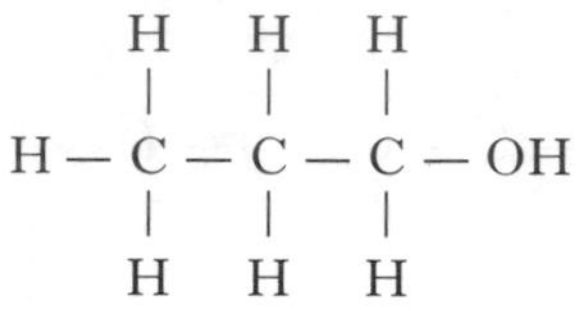	7	no effect
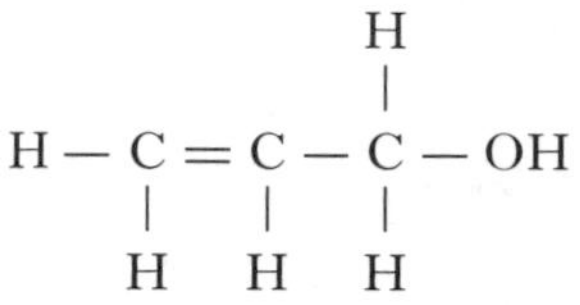	7	decolourised

Which line in the table below shows the correct results for the following compound?

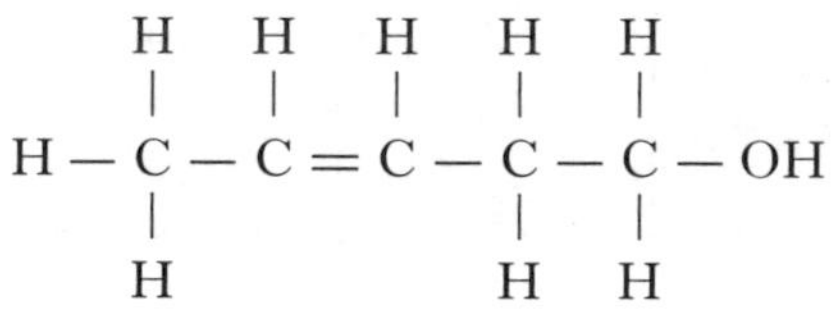

	pH of aqueous solution	**Effect on bromine solution**
A	4	decolourised
B	7	decolourised
C	4	no effect
D	7	no effect

13. Poly(ethenol) is

    A   a natural polymer, which is insoluble in water

    B   a natural polymer, which is soluble in water

    C   a synthetic polymer, which is soluble in water

    D   a synthetic polymer, which is insoluble in water.

14. Part of the structure of a polymer is drawn below.

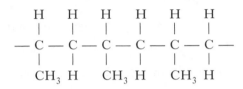

    The repeating unit of this polymer is

    A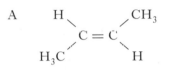

    B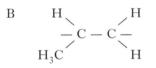

    C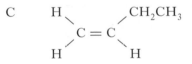

    D   H $\backslash$ CH$_2$CH$_3$ — C — C — H H

15. Which sugar will **not** be detected by the Benedict's test?

    A   Fructose

    B   Glucose

    C   Maltose

    D   Sucrose

16. The structure of glycerol is

    A   OH
         |
    H — C — H
         |
         H

    B   OH OH
         | |
    H — C — C — H
         | |
         H   H

    C   OH OH OH
         | | |
    H — C — C — C — H
         | | |
         H   H   H

    D   OH OH OH OH
         | | | |
    H — C — C — C — C — H
         | | | |
         H   II   H   H

17. The conversion of an oil into a hardened fat involves the

    A   removal of hydrogen

    B   addition of hydrogen

    C   removal of water

    D   addition of water.

18. Which of the following oxides, when shaken with water, would leave the pH unchanged?

    (You may wish to use page 5 of the data booklet to help you.)

    A   Carbon dioxide

    B   Copper oxide

    C   Sodium oxide

    D   Sulphur dioxide

19. Which of the following **increases** when hydrochloric acid is diluted with water?

    A   Rate of reaction with magnesium

    B   Concentration of H$^+$ ions

    C   Electrical conductivity

    D   pH

20. Which of the following statements describes the concentrations of $H^+(aq)$ and $OH^-(aq)$ ions in pure water?

A   The concentrations of $H^+(aq)$ and $OH^-(aq)$ ions are equal.

B   The concentrations of $H^+(aq)$ and $OH^-(aq)$ ions are zero.

C   The concentration of $H^+(aq)$ ions is greater than the concentration of $OH^-(aq)$ ions.

D   The concentration of $OH^-(aq)$ ions is greater than the concentration of $H^+(aq)$ ions.

21. When $100\,cm^3$ of a $1\,mol\,l^{-1}$ solution of sodium sulphate was evaporated to dryness, $14\cdot2\,g$ of solid was obtained.

To obtain $14\cdot2\,g$ of solid from a $2\,mol\,l^{-1}$ solution of sodium sulphate the volume of solution needed would be

A $25\,cm^3$

B $50\,cm^3$

C $100\,cm^3$

D $200\,cm^3$.

22. In which of the following test tubes will a gas be produced?

A

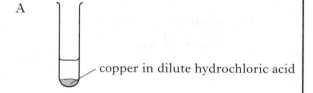

copper in dilute hydrochloric acid

B

copper oxide in dilute hydrochloric acid

C

copper carbonate in dilute hydrochloric acid

D

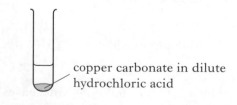

copper hydroxide in dilute hydrochloric acid

23. Which of the following compounds would **not** be used as a fertiliser?

A NH_4NO_3

B KNO_3

C   NaCl

D K_3PO_4

24. Which of the following solutions would produce a precipitate when mixed together?

(You may wish to use page 5 of the data booklet to help you.)

A   Ammonium chloride and potassium nitrate

B   Zinc nitrate and magnesium sulphate

C   Calcium nitrate and nickel chloride

D   Sodium iodide and silver nitrate

25. Sodium sulphate solution reacts with barium chloride solution.

$$Na_2SO_4(aq) + BaCl_2(aq) \rightarrow BaSO_4(s) + 2NaCl(aq)$$

The spectator ions present in this reaction are

A Na^+ and Cl^-

B Na^+ and SO_4^{2-}

C Ba^{2+} and Cl^-

D Ba^{2+} and SO_4^{2-}.

26. Which of the following solutions will react with magnesium metal?

A   Magnesium chloride

B   Zinc chloride

C   Potassium chloride

D   Sodium chloride

27. Which of the following cells would produce the highest voltage?

(You may wish to use page 7 of the data booklet to help you.)

A

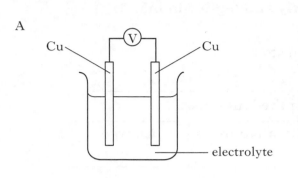

B

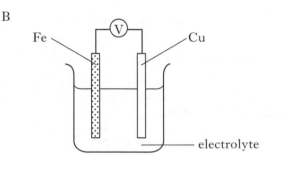

C

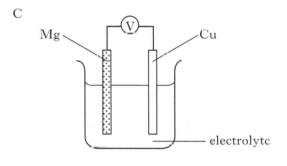

D

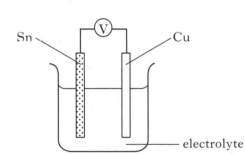

28.

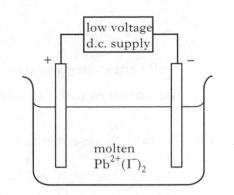

Which of the following describes the reaction at the positive electrode?

A I^- reduced

B I^- oxidised

C Pb^{2+} oxidised

D Pb^{2+} reduced

29. The table contains information about calcium and calcium chloride.

	Melting point (°C)	Density (g cm^{-3})
Calcium	842	1·54
Calcium chloride	772	2·15

When molten calcium chloride is electrolysed at 800 °C the calcium appears as a

A   solid on the surface of the molten calcium chloride

B   liquid on the surface of the molten calcium chloride

C   solid at the bottom of the molten calcium chloride

D   liquid at the bottom of the molten calcium chloride.

30. Which ion will turn ferroxyl indicator pink?

A $Fe^{2+}(aq)$

B $Fe^{3+}(aq)$

C $H^+(aq)$

D $OH^-(aq)$

Candidates are reminded that the answer sheet for Section A MUST be placed INSIDE the front cover of this answer book.

Marks

SECTION B

50 marks are available in this section of the paper.

All answers must be written clearly and legibly in ink.

1. The diagram represents the structure of an atom.

In the Nucleus

Name of particle	Relative mass	Charge
Proton		+1
Neutron	1	

Outside the Nucleus

Name of particle	Relative mass	Charge
	almost zero	

(a) Complete the tables.   2

(b) Ernest Rutherford used alpha particles to confirm the structure of the atom. The table shows the number of protons, electrons and neutrons in an alpha particle.

	Number
Proton	2
Electron	0
Neutron	2

(i) What is the atomic number of an alpha particle?

_____   1

Marks

1. (*b*) (continued)

(ii) When alpha particles are passed through an electric field, which letter in the diagram shows the path taken by them?

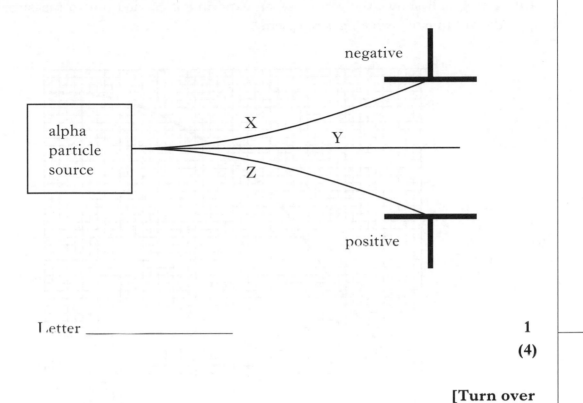

Letter _____

1

(4)

[Turn over

Marks

2. Hydrogen peroxide solution decomposes to give water and oxygen.

$$2H_2O_2(aq) \rightarrow 2H_2O(\ell) + O_2(g)$$

(a) The graph shows the results of an experiment carried out to measure the volume of oxygen gas released.

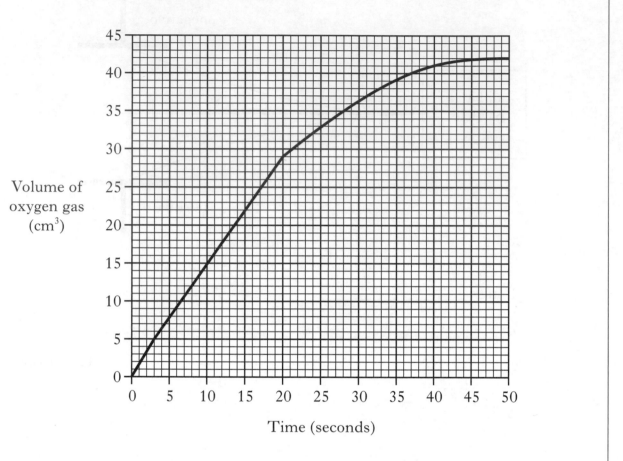

Time (seconds)

Calculate the average rate of reaction between 0 and 20 seconds.

_____ $cm^3 s^{-1}$ **1**

(b) The reaction was catalysed by a **solution** of Fe^{3+} ions which is amber in colour.

   (i) Why is the term homogeneous used to describe this catalyst?

   _____

   _____   **1**

   (ii) What colour would the solution be at the end of the reaction?

   _____   **1**

Marks

3. Tin and its compounds have many uses.

(a) Why do metals such as tin conduct electricity?

_____

_____ 1

(b) Tin(IV) chloride, $SnCl_4$, is used in the processing of glass and can be prepared as shown.

$$SnO_2 \;+\; 4HCl \;\rightarrow\; SnCl_4 \;+\; 2H_2O$$

  (i) Name the type of reaction taking place.

_____ 1

  (ii) Tin(IV) chloride is a liquid at room temperature and is made up of discrete molecules.

What type of bonding does this suggest is present in tin(IV) chloride?

_____ 1

(3)

[Turn over

Marks

4. Magnesium reacts with dilute hydrochloric acid.

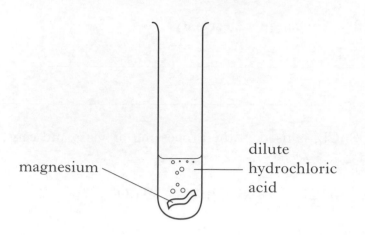

The equation for the reaction is shown.

$$Mg(s) \;+\; 2HCl(aq) \;\rightarrow\; MgCl_2(\;\;) \;+\; H_2(g)$$

(*a*) (i) Complete the equation by adding the state symbol for magnesium chloride.

(You may wish to use page 5 of the data booklet to help you.)   **1**

(ii) State the test for hydrogen gas.

_____   **1**

(*b*) In an experiment 4·9 g of magnesium reacted with excess dilute hydrochloric acid. Calculate the mass of hydrogen produced in this reaction.

_____ g   **2**

(4)

Marks

5. Thiols are organic compounds containing sulphur. Some thiols are listed in the table.

Formula	Name of thiol
CH_3SH	methanethiol
CH_3CH_2SH	ethanethiol
CH_3 | CH_3CHCH_2SH	**X**
CH_3 | $CH_3CHCH_2CH_2SH$	3-methylbutane-1-thiol

(*a*) Ethanethiol is added to natural gas to give it a smell.
Draw the **full** structural formula for ethanethiol.

1

(*b*) Suggest the name for thiol **X**.

_____   1

(*c*) Thiols undergo complete combustion.

thiols + oxygen → carbon dioxide + water + _____

Complete the word equation for this reaction.   1

(3)

[Turn over

Marks

6. A student completed the **PPA "Testing for Unsaturation"**. Results from the experiment are shown in the table.

Hydrocarbon	Molecular formula	Observation with bromine solution	Saturated or unsaturated
A	C_6H_{14}	no change	
B	C_6H_{12}		unsaturated
C	C_6H_{12}		saturated
D	C_6H_{10}	bromine decolourises	

(a) Complete the table.

2

(b) Care had to be taken when using bromine solution. Give a safety precaution, **other** than eye protection, which should be taken when completing this PPA.

_____ 1

(c) Suggest a possible name for hydrocarbon **B**.

_____ 1

(4)

Marks

7. Polystyrene is made from the monomer, styrene. The systematic name for styrene is phenylethene.

$$CH = CH_2$$
$$|$$
$$C_6H_5$$

Styrene (phenylethene)

(a) The monomer used to form polystyrene is shown.

Which part of the structure of styrene allows the polymer to form?

_____   1

(b) Complete the diagram to show how three styrene molecules join to form part of the polymer chain.

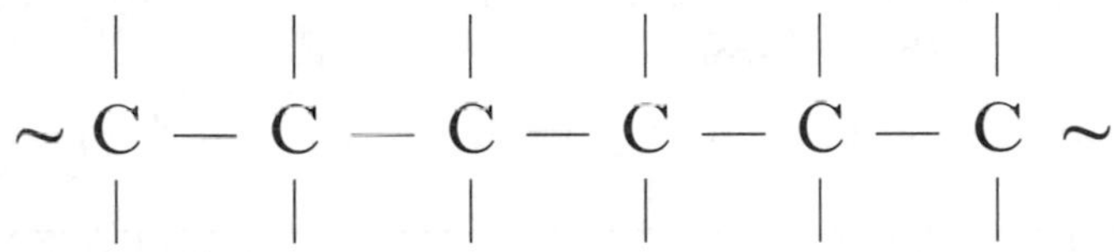

$$\sim C - C - C - C - C - C \sim$$

1

(c) Give another name for polystyrene.

_____   1
                                                    (3)

[Turn over

Marks

8. The fermentation of glucose is catalysed by the enzyme zymase.

$$C_6H_{12}O_6(aq) \rightarrow C_2H_5OH(aq) + CO_2(g)$$

(*a*) Balance the equation.   1

(*b*) A series of fermentation experiments was carried out at different temperatures and the volume of carbon dioxide was measured.

Experiment	Temperature (°C)	Volume of CO_2 (cm^3)
1	15	8
2	20	25
3	25	35
4	30	42
5	35	27
6	40	14

(i) Plot a line graph of these results, showing the temperature of the reaction against the volume of CO_2 collected.

(Additional graph paper, if required, will be found on page 28.)

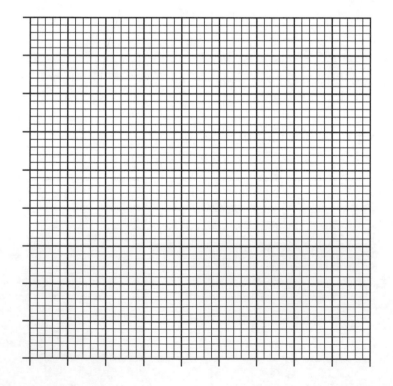

2

(ii) When the experiment was carried out at 70 °C, no carbon dioxide was produced.

Suggest a reason for this.

_____   1

Marks

9. When a hydrocarbon is burnt, carbon dioxide and water are produced. The following experiment can be used to investigate the products of combustion.

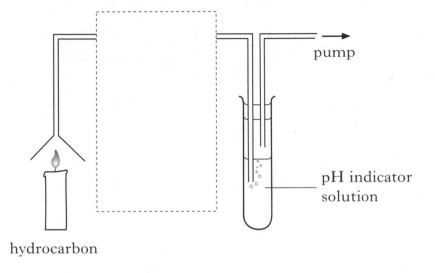

pump

pH indicator
solution

hydrocarbon

(a) Complete the diagram to show the apparatus which would be used to collect the water.

1

(b) When the carbon dioxide produced in the reaction is passed through the pH indicator solution, the solution turns from green to red.

What does this colour change suggest about carbon dioxide?

_____

1

(2)

[Turn over

DO NOT
WRITE IN
THIS
MARGIN

Marks

10. The silk that spiders spin into a web is made from a protein called fibroin. Two of the amino acids spiders use to make this protein are glycine and alanine.

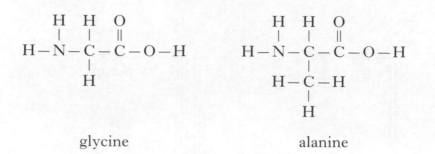

glycine   alanine

When fibroin is formed, the glycine and alanine are joined by a peptide link. Part of the structure of the protein is shown below.

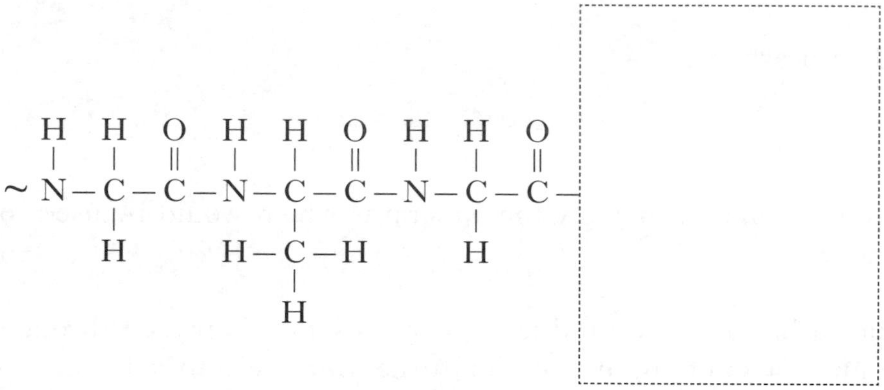

(a) Circle a peptide link in the protein structure.   1

(b) Complete the structure by adding another molecule of **glycine**.   1

(c) Name the type of polymerisation that produces fibroin.

_____   1

                                                         (3)

Marks

11. The Statue of Liberty is made from copper attached to an iron frame.

Statue of Liberty

(*a*) Why does the iron frame rust more quickly when attached to the copper?

_____

_____

_____   1

(*b*) The statue sits on an island surrounded by seawater.

Why does the seawater increase the rate of rusting?

_____

_____

_____   1

(*c*) Rust contains iron(III) oxide.

Write the formula for iron(III) oxide.

_____   1

(3)

[Turn over

Marks

12. Electrolysis of molten sodium hydride produces hydrogen gas.

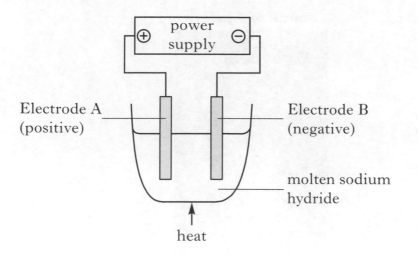

The ion-electron equations taking place at the electrodes are:

$$Na^+ + e^- \rightarrow Na$$

$$2H^- \rightarrow H_2 + 2e^-$$

(a) Use the equations to identify the electrode at which hydrogen gas is produced.

_____   **1**

(b) Combine the two ion-electron equations to give the **balanced** redox equation.

_____   **1**

(c) Sodium hydride reacts with water to form a solution of sodium hydroxide.

Sodium hydroxide is an example of a strong base.

Complete the table by circling the correct words to show how the properties of sodium hydroxide solution compare with ammonia solution, which is a weak base.

	$0.1 \ mol \ l^{-1}$ ammonia solution	$0.1 \ mol \ l^{-1}$ sodium hydroxide solution	
pH	10	lower	higher
Current in a conductivity cell (microamps)	22	lower	higher

1

(3)

Marks

13.

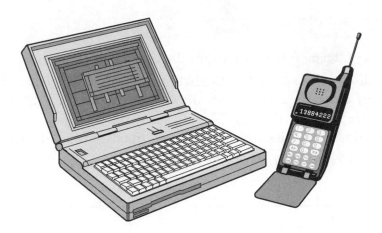

Lithium cells are used as batteries in laptops and mobile phones. In these cells lithium is present as ions.

(*a*)   (i)   Write the electron arrangement for the lithium **ion**.

1

      (ii)   Suggest an advantage of using lithium **ions** rather than lithium atoms in the cell.

_____

1

(*b*)   The voltages of cells can be measured. Some voltages of cells in which different metals are connected to copper are shown in the table.

Metal connected to copper	Voltage (V)
Iron	0·44
Lead	0·13
Lithium	3·02

State the relationship between the position of the metal in the electrochemical series and voltage.

_____

1

(3)

[Turn over

Marks

14. Titanium is an important metal.

(*a*) Titanium can be extracted from titanium dioxide.

The titanium dioxide is reacted with carbon and chlorine to produce impure titanium chloride and carbon dioxide. The impure titanium chloride is purified by distillation. Magnesium metal is added to the pure titanium chloride producing titanium and magnesium chloride.

Complete the flow chart to show the extraction process.

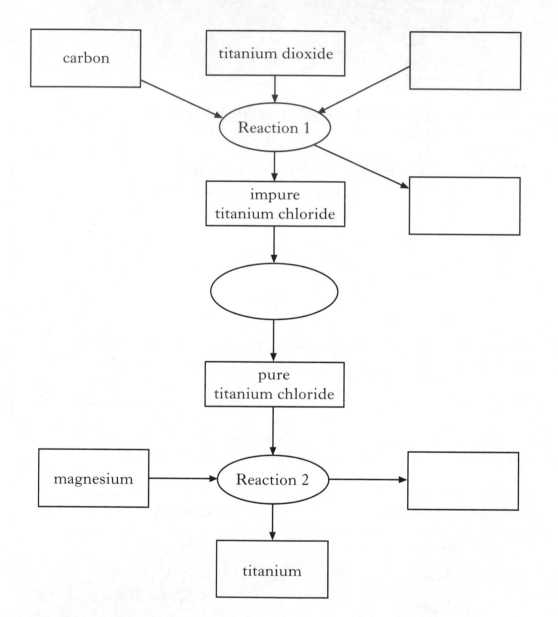

2

Marks

14. (continued)

(b) A mixture of titanium and nickel is used to make the alloy, Nitinol. This alloy is used to make dental braces.

The composition of Nitinol is shown in the table.

Metal	titanium	nickel
percentage by mass	45	55

A set of braces has a mass of 8 g.

(i) Calculate the mass of titanium in the braces.

_____ g   1

(ii) Calculate the number of moles of titanium in the braces.
(Relative atomic mass of titanium = 48)

_____   1

(4)

Marks

15. A student carried out a **PPA** to prepare the salt, magnesium sulphate.

(*a*) Name the acid used to make this salt.

_____

1

(*b*) Part of the student's PPA assessment sheet is shown.

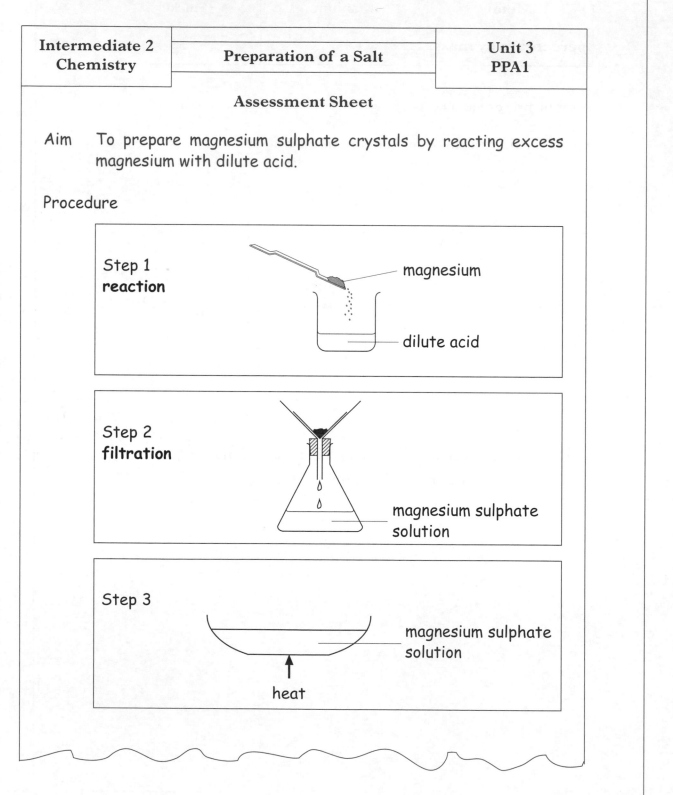

Intermediate 2 Chemistry	Preparation of a Salt	Unit 3 PPA1

Assessment Sheet

Aim   To prepare magnesium sulphate crystals by reacting excess magnesium with dilute acid.

Procedure

Step 1 **reaction** — magnesium / dilute acid

Step 2 **filtration** — magnesium sulphate solution

Step 3 — magnesium sulphate solution / heat

Marks

15. (*b*) **(continued)**

(i) Why was the reaction mixture filtered in step 2?

_____   1

(ii) There are three steps in the preparation of magnesium sulphate.

Step 1   reaction

Step 2   filtration

Step 3   _____

Name step 3.   1

(*c*) The diagram shows the chemical energies of the reactants and products when magnesium reacts with dilute acid.

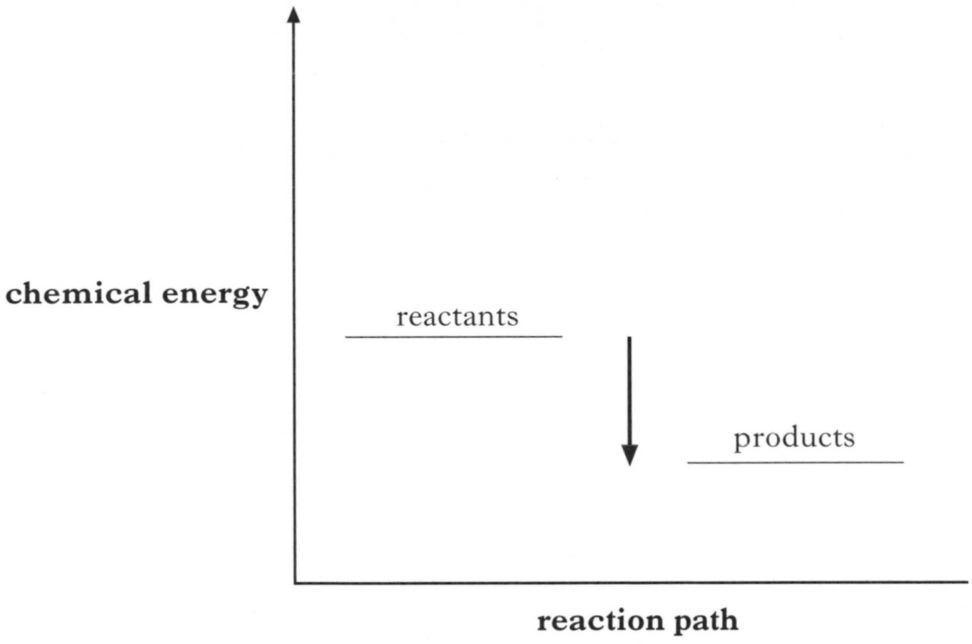

In what way does the energy diagram show that the reaction is exothermic?

_____

_____

_____   1

(4)

[END OF QUESTION PAPER]

ADDITIONAL SPACE FOR ANSWERS

ADDITIONAL GRAPH PAPER FOR QUESTION 8(*b*)(i)

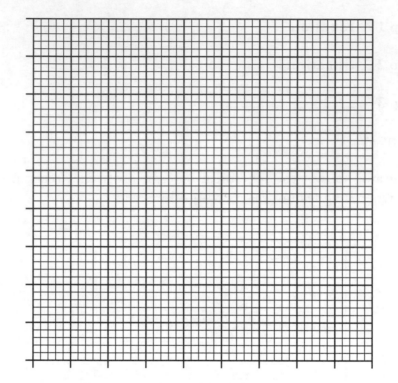

ADDITIONAL SPACE FOR ANSWERS

ADDITIONAL SPACE FOR ANSWERS

ADDITIONAL SPACE FOR ANSWERS

[BLANK PAGE]

[BLANK PAGE]

FOR OFFICIAL USE

Section B   **Total Marks**

X012/201

NATIONAL
QUALIFICATIONS
2008

FRIDAY, 30 MAY
9.00 AM – 11.00 AM

CHEMISTRY
INTERMEDIATE 2

Fill in these boxes and read what is printed below.

Full name of centre

Town

Forename(s)

Surname

Date of birth
Day   Month   Year   Scottish candidate number   Number of seat

Necessary data will be found in the Chemistry Data Booklet for Standard Grade and Intermediate 2.

Section A — Questions 1—30 (30 marks)

Instructions for completion of **Section A** are given on page two.

For this section of the examination you must use an **HB pencil**.

Section B (50 marks)

All questions should be attempted.

The questions may be answered in any order but all answers are to be written in the spaces provided in this answer book, **and must be written clearly and legibly in ink**.

Rough work, if any should be necessary, should be written in this book, and then scored through when the fair copy has been written. If further space is required, a supplementary sheet for rough work may be obtained from the invigilator.

Additional space for answers will be found at the end of the book. If further space is required, supplementary sheets may be obtained from the invigilator and should be inserted inside the **front** cover of this booklet.

Before leaving the examination room you must give this book to the invigilator. If you do not, you may lose all the marks for this paper.

Read carefully

1 Check that the answer sheet provided is for **Chemistry Intermediate 2 (Section A)**.

2 For this section of the examination you must use an **HB pencil** and, where necessary, an eraser.

3 Check that the answer sheet you have been given has **your name**, **date of birth**, **SCN** (Scottish Candidate Number) and **Centre Name** printed on it.

   Do not change any of these details.

4 If any of this information is wrong, tell the Invigilator immediately.

5 If this information is correct, **print** your name and seat number in the boxes provided.

6 The answer to each question is **either** A, B, C or D. Decide what your answer is, then, using your pencil, put a horizontal line in the space provided (see sample question below).

7 There is **only one correct** answer to each question.

8 Any rough working should be done on the question paper or the rough working sheet, **not** on your answer sheet.

9 At the end of the exam, put the **answer sheet for Section A inside the front cover of this answer book**.

Sample Question

To show that the ink in a ball-pen consists of a mixture of dyes, the method of separation would be

   A chromatography

   B fractional distillation

   C fractional crystallisation

   D filtration.

The correct answer is **A**—chromatography. The answer **A** has been clearly marked in **pencil** with a horizontal line (see below).

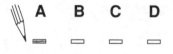

Changing an answer

If you decide to change your answer, carefully erase your first answer and using your pencil, fill in the answer you want. The answer below has been changed to **D**.

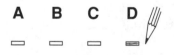

SECTION A

1. Which of the following pairs of reactants would produce hydrogen most slowly?

   A   Magnesium powder and 4 mol l^{-1} acid

   B   Magnesium ribbon and 2 mol l^{-1} acid

   C   Magnesium powder and 2 mol l^{-1} acid

   D   Magnesium ribbon and 4 mol l^{-1} acid

2. Vinegar can be made by dissolving ethanoic acid in water.

   Which term describes the water used when making the vinegar?

   A   Solute

   B   Saturated

   C   Solvent

   D   Solution

3. Which of the following is an element?

   A   Ammonia

   B   Carbon dioxide

   C   Fluorine

   D   Methane

4. An atom is neutral because

   A   the number of electrons equals the total number of protons plus neutrons

   B   the number of neutrons equals the total number of electrons plus protons

   C   the number of protons equals the number of neutrons

   D   the number of electrons equals the number of protons.

5. Which of the following is the electron arrangement for a noble gas?

   (You may wish to use page 1 of the data booklet to help you.)

   A   2, 5

   B   2, 6

   C   2, 7

   D   2, 8

6. The table shows information about an **ion**.

Particle	Number
protons	19
neutrons	20
electrons	18

   The charge on the ion is

   A   1+

   B   1–

   C   2+

   D   2–.

7. Which of the following diagrams could be used to represent the structure of a metal?

   A
   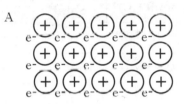

   B
   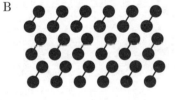

   C
   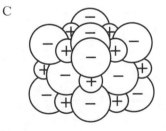

   D
   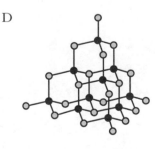

8. When methane burns in a plentiful supply of air, the products are

   A   carbon monoxide and water vapour

   B   carbon and water vapour

   C   carbon dioxide and hydrogen

   D   carbon dioxide and water vapour.

9. How many moles are present in $1 \cdot 7$ g of ammonia, NH_3?

   A $0 \cdot 1$

   B $1 \cdot 0$

   C $1 \cdot 7$

   D   17

10. Which line in the table shows the properties of an ionic compound?

	Melting point (°C)	Boiling point (°C)	Conducts electricity?	
			Solid	Liquid
A	181	1347	yes	yes
B	−95	69	no	no
C	686	1330	no	yes
D	1700	2230	no	no

11. The fractional distillation of crude oil produces a number of different fractions.

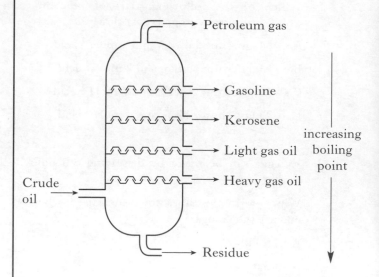

   Compared with the gasoline fraction, the heavy gas oil fraction is

   A   less viscous and evaporates more readily

   B   more viscous and evaporates more readily

   C   less viscous and evaporates less readily

   D   more viscous and evaporates less readily.

12.

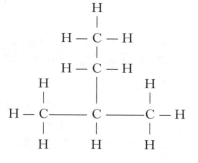

   The name of the above compound is

   A   1, 1–dimethylpropane

   B   2-ethylpropane

   C   2-methylbutane

   D   3-methylbutane.

13. Which of the following compounds fits the general formula, C_nH_{2n}, and will rapidly decolourise bromine solution?

   A   Cyclopentane

   B   Cyclopentene

   C   Pentane

   D   Pentene

14. Three members of the cycloalkene homologous series are:

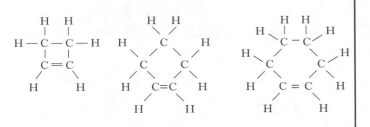

The general formula for this homologous series is

A C_nH_{2n+2}

B C_nH_{2n}

C C_nH_{2n-2}

D C_nH_{2n-4}.

15. Which of the following molecules is an isomer of heptane?

A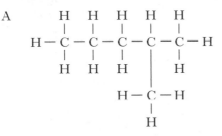

B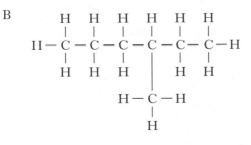

C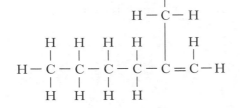

D

16. Fermentation of glucose to ethanol and carbon dioxide by yeast stops when the ethanol concentration reaches about 13%.

This is because

A the ethanol has destroyed the yeast

B all the glucose has been used up

C carbon dioxide is harmful to yeast

D the mixture is now saturated with ethanol.

17.

methanol + ethanoic acid → methyl ethanoate + water

This reaction is an example of

A addition

B dehydration

C condensation

D neutralisation.

18. The flow diagram shows the manufacture of polythene from hydrocarbons in crude oil.

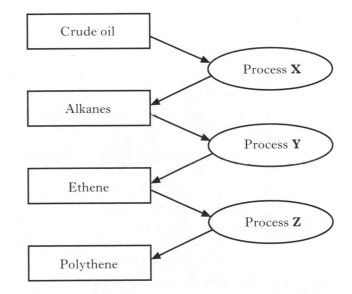

Which line in the table identifies processes X, Y and Z?

	Process X	Process Y	Process Z
A	distillation	cracking	hydrolysis
B	cracking	combustion	polymerisation
C	polymerisation	distillation	hydrolysis
D	distillation	cracking	polymerisation

19. Which of the following structures is that of an amino acid?

A

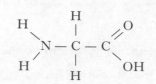

B

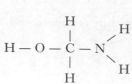

C

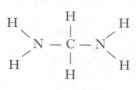

D

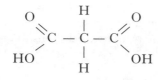

20. Compared with oils, fats are

    A   less saturated and have higher melting points

    B   less saturated and have lower melting points

    C   more saturated and have higher melting points

    D   more saturated and have lower melting points.

21. A neutral solution contains

    A   neither hydrogen ions nor hydroxide ions

    B   equal numbers of hydrogen ions and hydroxide ions

    C   more hydrogen ions than hydroxide ions

    D   more hydroxide ions than hydrogen ions.

22. Which of the following oxides will dissolve in water to produce an alkaline solution?

    (You may wish to use page 5 of the data booklet to help you.)

    A   Carbon dioxide

    B   Copper(II) oxide

    C   Potassium oxide

    D   Nitrogen dioxide

23. 1 mole of sodium chloride can be used to prepare

    A $250 \, cm^3$ of a $0 \cdot 4 \, mol \, l^{-1}$ solution

    B $250 \, cm^3$ of a $4 \, mol \, l^{-1}$ solution

    C $200 \, cm^3$ of a $0 \cdot 5 \, mol \, l^{-1}$ solution

    D $200 \, cm^3$ of a $1 \, mol \, l^{-1}$ solution.

24. Compared to a $1 \, mol \, l^{-1}$ solution of hydrochloric acid, a $1 \, mol \, l^{-1}$ solution of ethanoic acid will

    A   have a higher pH and react more slowly with magnesium

    B   have a higher pH and react more quickly with magnesium

    C   have a lower pH and react more slowly with magnesium

    D   have lower pH and react more quickly with magnesium.

25. Hydrogen gas

    A   burns with a pop

    B   relights a glowing splint

    C   turns damp pH paper red

    D   turns limewater cloudy.

26.

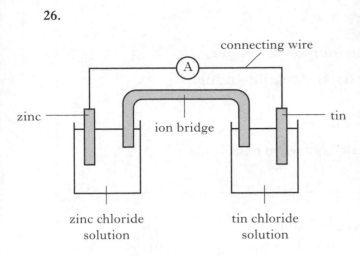

In the cell shown, electrons flow through

A   the solution from tin to zinc

B   the solution from zinc to tin

C   the connecting wire from tin to zinc

D   the connecting wire from zinc to tin.

27. Four cells were made by joining copper, iron, tin and zinc to silver. The voltages are shown in the table.

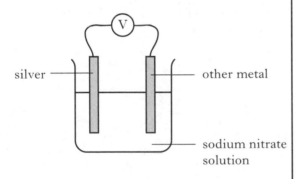

Which line in the table shows the voltage of the cell containing copper joined to silver?

(You may wish to use page 7 of the data booklet to help you.)

Cell	Voltage (V)
A	1·6
B	1·2
C	0·9
D	0·5

28. Which of the following metals is found uncombined in the Earth's crust?

A   Aluminium

B   Iron

C   Lead

D   Silver

29. Which ion gives a blue colour with ferroxyl indicator?

A $H^+(aq)$

B $OH^-(aq)$

C $Fe^{2+}(aq)$

D $Fe^{3+}(aq)$

30. Which of the following methods can give both physical and sacrificial protection to iron?

A   Painting

B   Greasing

C   Tin-plating

D   Galvanising

Candidates are reminded that the answer sheet for Section A MUST be placed INSIDE the front cover of this answer book.

DO NOT WRITE IN THIS MARGIN

Marks

SECTION B

50 marks are available in this section of the paper.

All answers must be written clearly and legibly in ink.

1. (*a*) To which family of metals does copper belong?

(You may wish to use page 8 of the data booklet to help you.)

____ **1**

(*b*) Copper is made up of two different types of atom.

(i) Complete the table to show the numbers of protons and neutrons in each type of copper atom.

	Number of protons	Number of neutrons
$^{63}_{29}Cu$		
$^{65}_{29}Cu$		

2

(ii) What term is used to describe the different types of copper atom?

____ **1**

(4)

Marks

2. The graph shows how the solubility of potassium chloride changes with temperature.

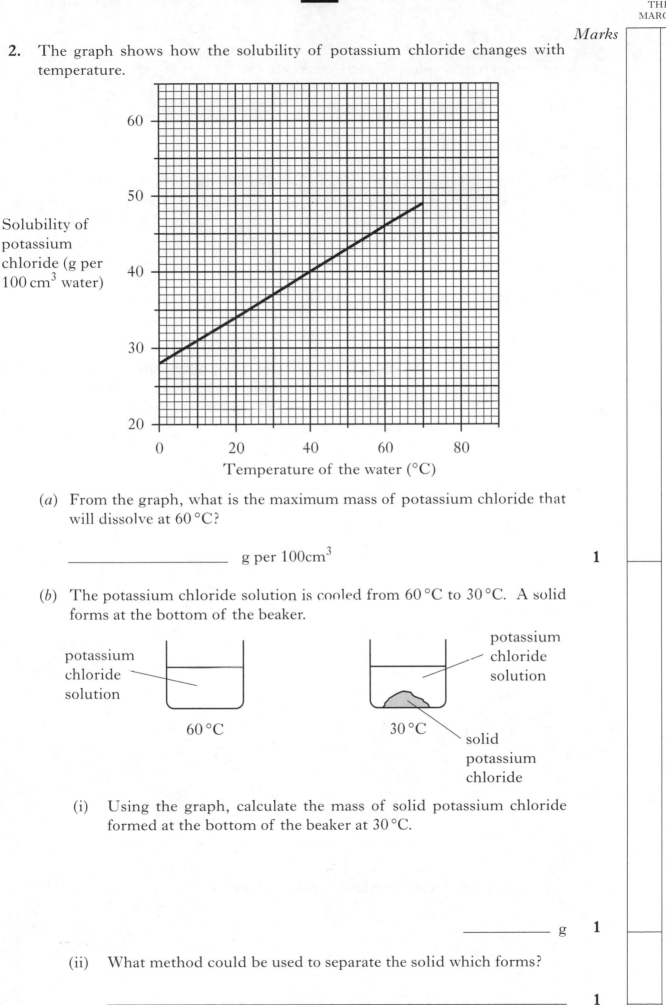

(a) From the graph, what is the maximum mass of potassium chloride that will dissolve at 60 °C?

_____ g per 100cm^3 1

(b) The potassium chloride solution is cooled from 60 °C to 30 °C. A solid forms at the bottom of the beaker.

(i) Using the graph, calculate the mass of solid potassium chloride formed at the bottom of the beaker at 30 °C.

_____ g   1

(ii) What method could be used to separate the solid which forms?

_____   1

(3)

[X012/201]   *Page nine*   **[Turn over**

Marks

3. When dinitrogen oxide, N_2O, is mixed with methane in the presence of a palladium catalyst, an explosive reaction takes place.

$$N_2O(g) \quad + \quad CH_4(g) \quad \rightarrow \quad N_2(g) \quad + \quad CO_2(g) \quad + \quad H_2O(g)$$

(a) Balance the above equation.

1

(b) Why can the palladium metal be described as a heterogeneous catalyst?

_____

_____

1

(c) The diagrams below show a possible model for palladium metal catalysing the reaction between dinitrogen oxide and methane.

Stage 1

N_2O CH_4

catalyst surface

Statement

Reactants are adsorbed on to the catalyst surface.

Stage 2

$$\quad\quad H \quad H$$
$$N\text{–}N \quad O \ H \ C \quad H$$

catalyst surface

Bonds break.

Stage 3

$$\quad\quad\quad\quad\quad O$$
$$N\text{=}N \quad H \ O\text{–}H \quad C\text{=}O$$

catalyst surface

New bonds form.

Stage 4

$$N_2 \quad\quad H_2O \quad\quad CO_2$$

_____

_____

catalyst surface   _____

Add a statement describing what happens at **Stage 4**.

1

Marks

3. **(continued)**

    (*d*) The presence of sulphur in methane gas can prevent the reaction from taking place.

    Why would the presence of sulphur prevent the catalyst from working?

    _____

    _____

    _____

    _____ **1**

    (4)

    [Turn over

Marks

4. In a **PPA**, a solution of copper (II) chloride was electrolysed.

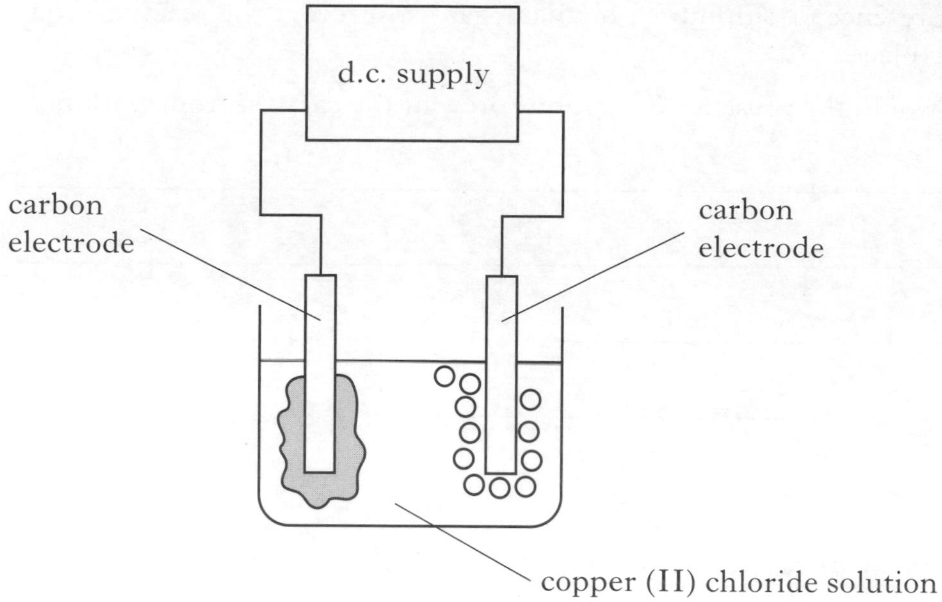

(a) What is meant by electrolysis?

_____

_____ 1

(b) Why is it necessary to use a d.c. supply in electrolysis?

_____

_____ 1

(c) (i) Complete the table by adding the charge for each electrode.

Observation at _____ electrode	Observation at _____ electrode
bubbles of gas	brown solid formed

1

(ii) How could the gas be identified?

_____

_____ 1

(4)

Marks

5.   Chlorofluorocarbons (CFCs) are a family of compounds which are highly effective as refrigerants and aerosol propellants.   However, they are now known to damage the ozone layer.

One example of a CFC molecule is shown.

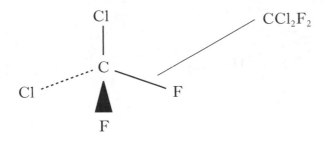

(a)   What term is used to describe the **shape** of this molecule?

_____   1

(b)   Scientists have developed compounds to replace CFCs.   The table shows information about the ratio of atoms in CCl_2F_2 and compounds used to replace it.

Compound	Number of atoms				Atmospheric life (years)
	C	Cl	F	H	
CCl_2F_2	1	2	2	0	102
Replacement 1	1	1	2	1	13·3
Replacement 2	2	0	4	2	14·6
Replacement 3	1	0	2	2	5·6

(i)   Draw a possible structure for Replacement 2.

1

(ii)   Compared with CCl_2F_2, the replacement compounds contain less of which element?

_____   1

(iii)   From the table, what is the advantage of using the replacement molecules as refrigerants and aerosol propellants?

_____   1

(4)

Marks

6. Poly(ethenol) is one of the substances used to cover dishwasher tablets.

A section of the poly(ethenol) polymer is shown.

$$-CH_2-CH-CH_2-CH-CH_2-CH-$$
$$\qquad\quad|\qquad\qquad|\qquad\qquad|$$
$$\qquad\ OH\qquad\quad OH\qquad\quad OH$$

(*a*) Name the functional group present in this polymer.

_____   1

(*b*) Draw the structure of the repeating unit for this polymer.

1

(*c*) A dishwasher tablet, complete with its poly(ethenol) cover, can be added to a dishwasher.

What property of the poly(ethenol) makes it suitable as a cover for a dishwasher tablet?

_____

_____   1

(3)

Marks

7. Scientists have replaced oils in gloss paints with synthetic polyesters. This has improved the drying quality of the paint.

The first step in the production of the synthetic polyester is shown.

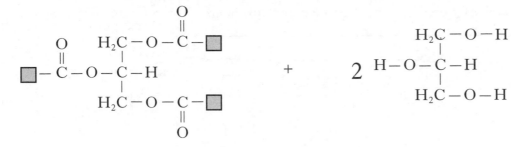

Triglyceride   **X**

Monoglyceride

(a) What does the term synthetic mean?

_____   1

(b) Circle an ester link in the triglyceride.   1

(c) Name **X**.

_____   1

                                                  (3)

[Turn over

Marks

8. Infrared spectroscopy can be used to detect the bonds present in molecules. The same bond always absorbs infrared radiation at the same wavenumber, even in different molecules.

For example, the C–H bond absorbs in the range 2800 – 3000 wavenumbers.

The infrared spectra of two different organic compounds are shown.

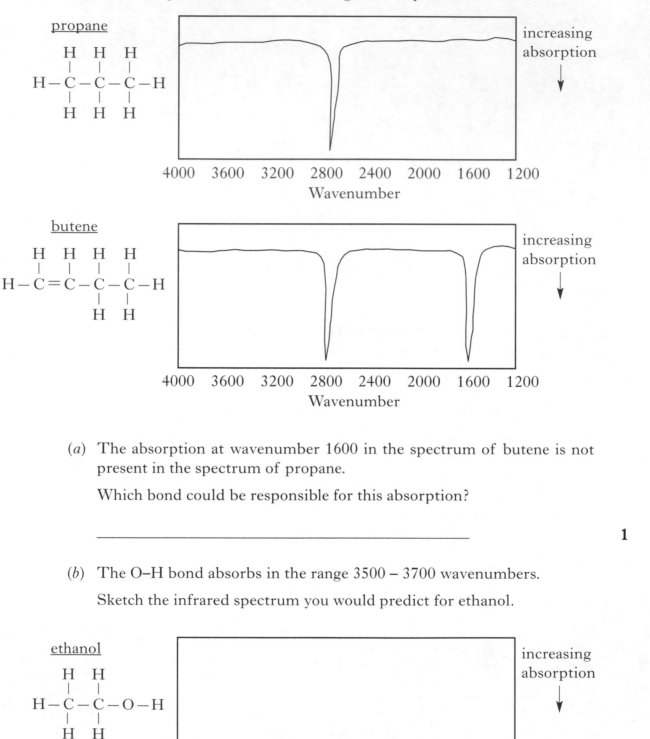

(a) The absorption at wavenumber 1600 in the spectrum of butene is not present in the spectrum of propane.

Which bond could be responsible for this absorption?

_____   **1**

(b) The O–H bond absorbs in the range 3500 – 3700 wavenumbers.

Sketch the infrared spectrum you would predict for ethanol.

1

(2)

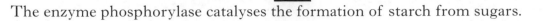

9. The enzyme phosphorylase catalyses the formation of starch from sugars.

(a) Name the monomer used to make a starch polymer.

_____

Marks

1

(b) Name the solution used to test for starch.

_____

1

(c) A student investigated the effect of temperature on the rate of starch formation. The results are shown.

Temperature (°C)	Relative rate 1/t (s^{-1})
4	0·003
12	0·010
16	0·016
20	0·022
24	0·033

(i) Plot these results as a line graph.
(Additional graph paper, if required, can be found on page 24.)

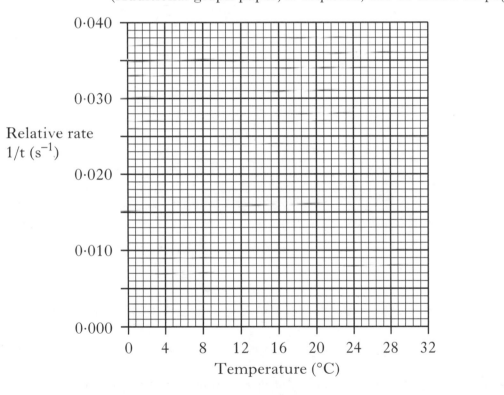

1

(ii) At 32 °C the relative rate was 0·0125 s^{-1}.
Use this rate to calculate the reaction time at 32 °C.

_____ seconds 1

(4)

Marks

10. **The Acid Test**
Adapted from Robert I. Wolke
November 2004

Seviche, a seafood dish, is described as "cooked" by marinating it in lime juice. Is it really "cooked" or is it still raw?

The citric acid in lime juice changes the proteins in fish. The normally twisted and folded protein molecules become unravelled and so the texture and colour of the fish change. This is known as denaturing.

Cooking also denatures proteins. The bonds that keep the protein twisted and folded are broken by heating the protein.

There are other methods which can be used to change the shape of proteins. Each method is complementary. For example, the stronger the acid that a protein is subjected to, the shorter the cooking time; the higher the temperature the shorter the cooking time.

Fish can therefore be cooked without heating it!

Use the article to answer the following questions.

(a) Proteins can be denatured.

Describe what happens to the protein when it is denatured.

_____

_____   1

(b) Other than heat, give a method that could be used to "cook" fish.

_____

_____   1

(c) Proteins can be denatured at low temperatures.

What does this suggest about the strength of the bonds keeping the protein twisted and folded?

_____

_____   1

(d) Draw a graph to show the relationship between cooking temperature and the cooking time for fish.

Cooking
temperature
(°C)

Cooking time

1

(4)

Marks

11. Silver jewellery slowly tarnishes in air. This is due to the formation of silver(I) sulphide.
    The silver(I) sulphide can be converted back to silver using the following apparatus.

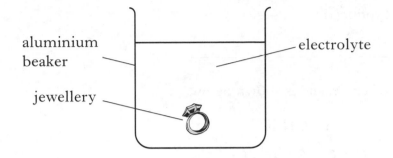

The equation for the reaction which takes place in the beaker is shown.

$$3Ag_2S(aq) \quad + \quad 2Al(s) \longrightarrow 6Ag(s) \quad + \quad Al_2S_3(aq)$$

(a) Calculate the mass of silver produced when $0.135\,g$ of aluminium is used up.

_____ g   **2**

(b) How would you show that aluminium has been lost from the beaker during this reaction?

_____   **1**

(3)

[Turn over

Marks

12. Many medicines are available as tablets which dissolve readily in water. These tablets contain solid citric acid and sodium hydrogencarbonate.

(a) When the tablet is added to water the citric acid reacts with the sodium hydrogencarbonate giving off a gas.

Name the gas produced.

_____   1

(b) The structure of citric acid is shown below.

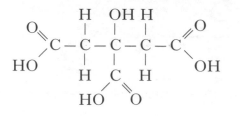

Write the molecular formula for citric acid.

_____   1

(c) In aqueous solution, citric acid molecules are only partially dissociated. What term is used to describe this type of acid?

_____   1
                                                    (3)

Marks

13. Strontium nitrate is used in fireworks. The flow chart shows how strontium nitrate can be produced.

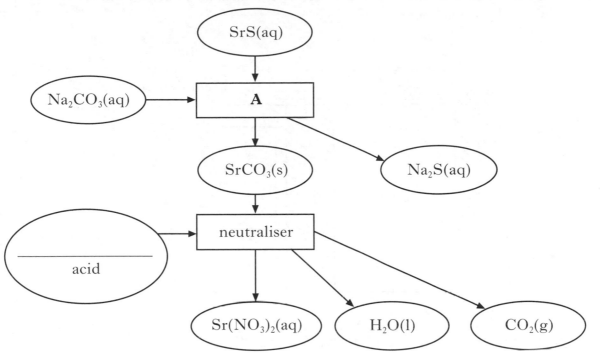

(a) Name the type of chemical reaction taking place at **A**.

_____   1

(b) Complete the flow chart by adding the name of the acid used to form the salt, strontium nitrate.

_____   1

(c) What colour would be seen when a firework containing strontium nitrate is set off?

(You may wish to use page 4 of the data booklet to help you.)

_____   1

  (3)

[Turn over

Marks

14. A number of electrochemical cells are being developed.

One such example is the aluminium/air cell. It is used as a back-up power supply in telephone exchanges.

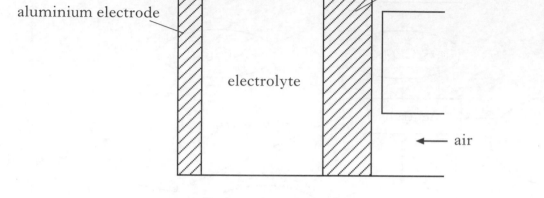

(a) What is the purpose of the electrolyte in the cell?

_____

_____   1

(b) The ion-electron equations for the reactions taking place at the electrodes are:

aluminium electrode	$Al \rightarrow Al^{3+} + 3e^-$
graphite electrode	$O_2 + 2H_2O + 4e^- \rightarrow 4OH^-$

(i) What process has the aluminium electrode undergone?

_____   1

(ii) When the cell is operating, a solid forms in the electrolyte.
Identify the solid.

(You may wish to use page 5 of the data booklet to help you.)

_____   1

(3)

Marks

15. A student's report is shown for the **PPA "Reactions of Metals with Oxygen"**.

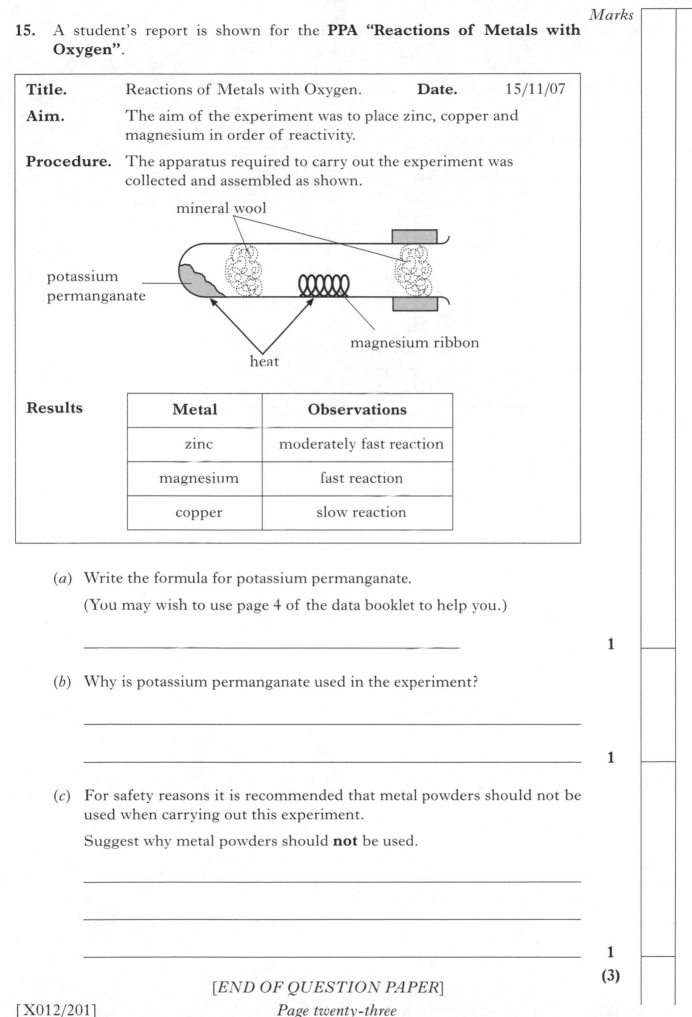

| Title. | Reactions of Metals with Oxygen. | **Date.** | 15/11/07 |

Aim. The aim of the experiment was to place zinc, copper and magnesium in order of reactivity.

Procedure. The apparatus required to carry out the experiment was collected and assembled as shown.

Results

Metal	Observations
zinc	moderately fast reaction
magnesium	fast reaction
copper	slow reaction

(a) Write the formula for potassium permanganate.

(You may wish to use page 4 of the data booklet to help you.)

_____   1

(b) Why is potassium permanganate used in the experiment?

_____

_____   1

(c) For safety reasons it is recommended that metal powders should not be used when carrying out this experiment.

Suggest why metal powders should **not** be used.

_____

_____

_____   1

   (3)

[END OF QUESTION PAPER]

ADDITIONAL SPACE FOR ANSWERS

ADDITIONAL GRAPH PAPER FOR QUESTION 9(c)(i)

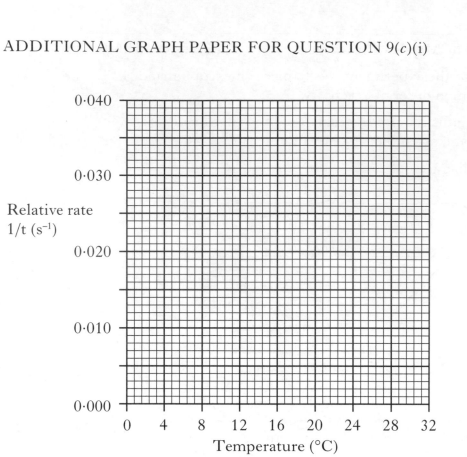

DO NOT
WRITE IN
THIS
MARGIN

ADDITIONAL SPACE FOR ANSWERS

ADDITIONAL SPACE FOR ANSWERS

DO NOT
WRITE IN
THIS
MARGIN

ADDITIONAL SPACE FOR ANSWERS

ADDITIONAL SPACE FOR ANSWERS

[BLANK PAGE]

[BLANK PAGE]

FOR OFFICIAL USE

Section B   Total Marks

X012/201

NATIONAL QUALIFICATIONS 2009

WEDNESDAY, 3 JUNE 9.00 AM – 11.00 AM

CHEMISTRY INTERMEDIATE 2

Fill in these boxes and read what is printed below.

Full name of centre

Town

Forename(s)

Surname

Date of birth
Day Month Year

Scottish candidate number

Number of seat

Necessary data will be found in the Chemistry Data Booklet for Standard Grade and Intermediate 2.

Section A — Questions 1—30 (30 marks)

Instructions for completion of **Section A** are given on page two.

For this section of the examination you must use an **HB pencil**.

Section B (50 marks)

All questions should be attempted.

The questions may be answered in any order but all answers are to be written in the spaces provided in this answer book, **and must be written clearly and legibly in ink**.

Rough work, if any should be necessary, should be written in this book, and then scored through when the fair copy has been written. If further space is required, a supplementary sheet for rough work may be obtained from the invigilator.

Additional space for answers will be found at the end of the book. If further space is required, supplementary sheets may be obtained from the invigilator and should be inserted inside the **front** cover of this booklet.

Before leaving the examination room you must give this book to the invigilator. If you do not, you may lose all the marks for this paper.

Read carefully

1 Check that the answer sheet provided is for **Chemistry Intermediate 2 (Section A)**.

2 For this section of the examination you must use an **HB pencil** and, where necessary, an eraser.

3 Check that the answer sheet you have been given has **your name**, **date of birth**, **SCN** (Scottish Candidate Number) and **Centre Name** printed on it.

Do not change any of these details.

4 If any of this information is wrong, tell the Invigilator immediately.

5 If this information is correct, **print** your name and seat number in the boxes provided.

6 The answer to each question is **either** A, B, C or D. Decide what your answer is, then, using your pencil, put a horizontal line in the space provided (see sample question below).

7 There is **only one correct** answer to each question.

8 Any rough working should be done on the question paper or the rough working sheet, **not** on your answer sheet.

9 At the end of the exam, put the **answer sheet for Section A inside the front cover of this answer book**.

Sample Question

To show that the ink in a ball-pen consists of a mixture of dyes, the method of separation would be

        A chromatography

        B fractional distillation

        C fractional crystallisation

        D filtration.

The correct answer is **A**—chromatography. The answer **A** has been clearly marked in **pencil** with a horizontal line (see below).

Changing an answer

If you decide to change your answer, carefully erase your first answer and using your pencil, fill in the answer you want. The answer below has been changed to **D**.

A   B   C   D

SECTION A

1. Which of the following gases is a noble gas?

   A   Argon

   B   Oxygen

   C   Fluorine

   D   Nitrogen

2. Which line in the table correctly shows how the concentration of a solution changes by adding more solute or by adding more solvent?

	Adding solute	Adding solvent
A	concentration falls	concentration rises
B	concentration falls	concentration falls
C	concentration rises	concentration falls
D	concentration rises	concentration rises

3. Magnesium and zinc both react with hydrochloric acid.

   In which of the following experiments would the reaction rate be fastest?

   A
   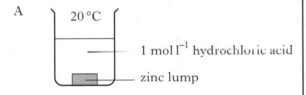
   20 °C

   1 mol l^{-1} hydrochloric acid

   zinc lump

   B
   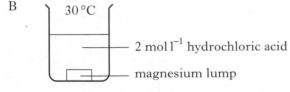
   30 °C

   2 mol l^{-1} hydrochloric acid

   magnesium lump

   C
   30 °C

   1 mol l^{-1} hydrochloric acid

   zinc powder

   D
   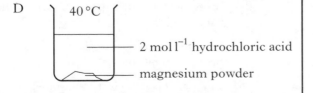
   40 °C

   2 mol l^{-1} hydrochloric acid

   magnesium powder

4. The table shows the numbers of protons, electrons and neutrons in four particles, **W**, **X**, **Y** and **Z**.

Particle	Protons	Electrons	Neutrons
W	17	17	18
X	11	11	12
Y	17	17	20
Z	18	18	18

   Which pair of particles are isotopes?

   A   **W** and **X**

   B   **W** and **Y**

   C   **X** and **Y**

   D   **Y** and **Z**

5. When solid sodium chloride dissolves in water, a solution containing sodium ions and chloride ions is formed.

   Which of the following equations correctly shows the state symbols for this process?

   A $NaCl(s) + H_2O(\ell) \rightarrow Na^+(\ell) + Cl^-(\ell)$

   B $NaCl(s) + H_2O(\ell) \rightarrow Na^+(aq) + Cl^-(aq)$

   C $NaCl(s) + H_2O(aq) \rightarrow Na^+(aq) + Cl^-(aq)$

   D $NaCl(aq) + H_2O(\ell) \rightarrow Na^+(aq) + Cl^-(aq)$

6. Metallic bonding is a force of attraction between

   A   positive ions and delocalised electrons

   B   negative ions and delocalised electrons

   C   negative ions and positive ions

   D   a shared pair of electrons and two nuclei.

[Turn over

7. The table gives information about the attraction some atoms have for bonded electrons.

Atom	Attraction for electrons
C	least
I	
Br	↓
Cl	
F	greatest

Which of the following bonds is the **least** polar?

A　C – F

B　C – Cl

C　C – Br

D　C – I

8. Which of the following diagrams represents a **compound** made up of **diatomic** molecules?

A

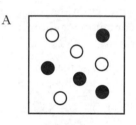

B

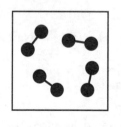

C

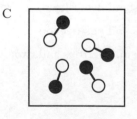

D

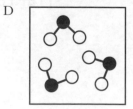

9. Which of the following diagrams could be used to represent the structure of sodium chloride?

A

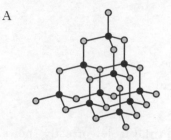

B

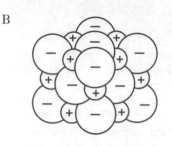

C

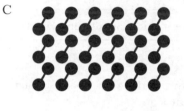

D

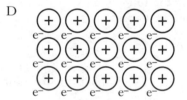

10.

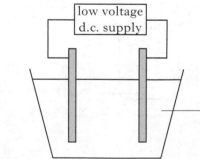

During the electrolysis of molten copper(II) bromide

A　copper atoms lose electrons to form copper ions

B　bromine molecules gain electrons to form bromide ions

C　bromide ions gain electrons to form bromine molecules

D　copper ions gain electrons to form copper atoms.

11. What is the name of the compound with the formula Ag_2O?

   A   Silver(I) oxide

   B   Silver(II) oxide

   C   Silver(III) oxide

   D   Silver(IV) oxide

12. Which of the following exhaust emissions is most likely to come from the incomplete combustion of diesel?

   A   Water vapour

   B   Soot particles

   C   Carbon dioxide

   D   Nitrogen dioxide

13. The apparatus shown can be used to identify what is produced when a gas is burned.

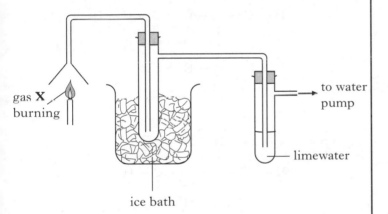

When gas **X** was burned, a colourless liquid collected in the cooled test tube but there was no change in the limewater.

Gas **X** could be

   A   methane

   B   carbon monoxide

   C   hydrogen

   D   ethene.

14. The fractional distillation of crude oil produces a number of different fractions.

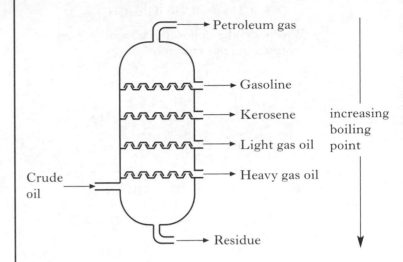

Compared with the heavy gas oil fraction, the kerosene fraction

   A   is less flammable and contains larger hydrocarbon molecules

   B   is less flammable and contains smaller hydrocarbon molecules

   C   is more flammable and contains larger hydrocarbon molecules

   D   is more flammable and contains smaller hydrocarbon molecules.

15. Which of the following could be the molecular formula of a cycloalkane?

   A C_7H_{10}

   B C_7H_{12}

   C C_7H_{14}

   D C_7H_{16}

[Turn over

16. The shortened structural formula for an organic compound is

$$CH_3CH(CH_3)CH(OH)C(CH_3)_3.$$

Which of the following is another way of representing this structure?

A
```
        H   H   OH  CH3
        |   |   |   |
   H — C — C — C — C — CH3
        |   |   |   |
        H   CH3 H   CH3
```

B
```
        H   H   H   OH  CH3
        |   |   |   |   |
   H — C — C — C — C — C — CH3
        |   |   |   |   |
        H   H   H   H   CH3
```

C
```
        H   H   H   CH3 CH3
        |   |   |   |   |
   H — C — C — C — C — C — H
        |   |   |   |   |
        H   CH3 OH  H   H
```

D
```
        H   H   H   H   H   H
        |   |   |   |   |   |
   H — C — C — C — C — C — C — CH3
        |   |   |   |   |   |
        H   CH3 OH  H   H   H
```

17.

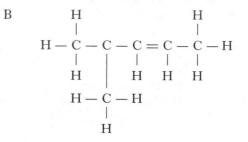

The above compound could be formed by adding water to

A

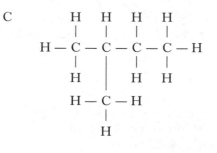

B

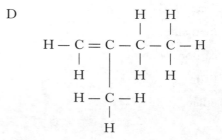

C
```
        H   H   H   H
        |   |   |   |
   H — C — C — C — C — H
        |   |   |   |
        H   |   H   H
        H — C — H
            |
            H
```

D
```
            H   H
            |   |
   H — C = C — C — C — H
        |   |   |   |
        H   |   H   H
        H — C — H
            |
            H
```

18. Part of the structure of an addition polymer is shown below. It is made using two different monomers.

$$-\overset{\overset{\displaystyle H}{|}}{\underset{\underset{\displaystyle H}{|}}{C}} - \overset{\overset{\displaystyle H}{|}}{\underset{\underset{\displaystyle H}{|}}{C}} - \overset{\overset{\displaystyle CH_3}{|}}{\underset{\underset{\displaystyle H}{|}}{C}} - \overset{\overset{\displaystyle H}{|}}{\underset{\underset{\displaystyle H}{|}}{C}} - \overset{\overset{\displaystyle H}{|}}{\underset{\underset{\displaystyle H}{|}}{C}} - \overset{\overset{\displaystyle H}{|}}{\underset{\underset{\displaystyle H}{|}}{C}} -$$

Which pair of alkenes could be used as monomers for this polymer?

A　Ethene and propene

B　Ethene and butene

C　Propene and butene

D　Ethene and pentene

19. In which of the following experiments would **both** carbohydrates give an orange precipitate when heated with Benedict's solution?

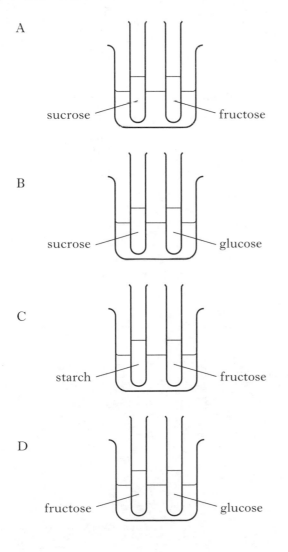

A

sucrose　　　fructose

B

sucrose　　　glucose

C

starch　　　fructose

D

fructose　　　glucose

20. Glycerol can be obtained from a fat by

A　hydrolysis

B　esterification

C　condensation

D　neutralisation.

21. Which oxide, when shaken with water, would leave the pH unchanged?

(You may wish to use page 5 of the data booklet to help you.)

A　Calcium oxide

B　Carbon dioxide

C　Sulphur dioxide

D　Zinc oxide

22. Two tests were carried out on compound **X**.

Test 1

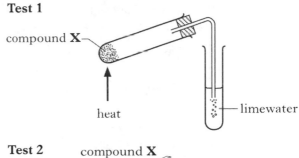

compound **X**

heat　　　limewater

Test 2　compound **X**

The following results were obtained.

Test	Result
1	limewater turns cloudy
2	flame turns blue-green

Which of the following could be compound **X**?

(You may wish to use page 4 of the data booklet to help you.)

A　Barium carbonate

B　Copper carbonate

C　Copper sulphate

D　Sodium sulphate

23. Which line in the table correctly shows the properties of $0.1\ mol\,l^{-1}$ ethanoic acid compared to $0.1\ mol\,l^{-1}$ hydrochloric acid?

	pH	Conductivity	Rate of reaction with magnesium
A	higher	lower	slower
B	lower	higher	faster
C	higher	higher	faster
D	lower	lower	slower

24. In water, an equilibrium exists between water molecules and hydrogen and hydroxide ions.

$$H_2O(\ell) \rightleftharpoons H^+(aq)\ +\ OH^-(aq)$$

At equilibrium

A the water molecules have stopped changing into ions

B the water molecules have all changed into ions

C the concentrations of water molecules and ions are equal

D the concentrations of water molecules and ions are constant.

25. $$2K^+(aq)\ +\ 2I^-(aq)\ +\ Pb^{2+}(aq)\ +\ 2NO_3^-(aq)$$
$$\downarrow$$
$$Pb^{2+}(I^-)_2(s)\ +\ 2K^+(aq)\ +\ 2NO_3^-(aq)$$

The type of reaction represented by the equation above is

A addition

B neutralisation

C precipitation

D redox.

26. Which of the following diagrams shows the apparatus which would allow a soluble gas to be removed from a mixture of gases?

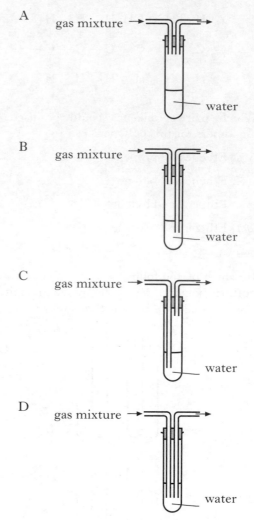

27. Which pair of metals, when connected in a cell, would give the highest voltage and a flow of electrons from **X** to **Y**?

(You may wish to use page 7 of the data booklet to help you.)

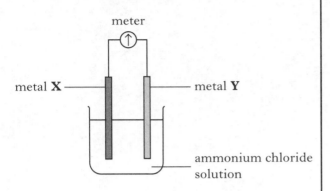

	Metal X	Metal Y
A	magnesium	copper
B	copper	magnesium
C	zinc	tin
D	tin	zinc

28. The ion-electron equation

$$Ti(s) \rightarrow Ti^{2+}(aq) + 2e^-$$

represents the

A reduction of titanium atoms

B reduction of titanium ions

C oxidation of titanium atoms

D oxidation of titanium ions.

29. The following statements relate to four different metals, **P**, **Q**, **R** and **S**.

Metal **P** displaces metal **Q** from a solution containing ions of **Q**.

In a cell, electrons flow from metal **S** to metal **P**.

Metal **R** is the only metal which can be obtained from its ore by heat alone.

The order of reactivity of the metals, starting with the **most** reactive is

A **S, P, Q, R**

B **R, Q, P, S**

C **R, S, Q, P**

D **S, Q, P, R**.

30.

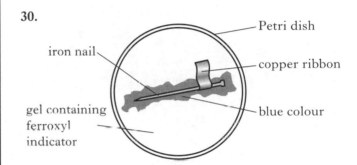

Which ion gives a blue colour with ferroxyl indicator?

A $OH^-(aq)$

B $Fe^{2+}(aq)$

C $Fe^{3+}(aq)$

D $Cu^{2+}(aq)$

Candidates are reminded that the answer sheet for Section A MUST be placed INSIDE the front cover of this answer book.

[Turn over

[BLANK PAGE]

Marks

SECTION B

50 marks are available in this section of the paper.

All answers must be written clearly and legibly in ink.

1. Atoms contain particles called protons, neutrons and electrons.

   The nuclide notation of the sodium atom is shown.

$$^{24}_{11}Na$$

   (a) Complete the table to show the number of each type of particle in this sodium atom.

Particle	Number
electron	11
proton	
neutron	

   1

   (b) Electrons are arranged in energy levels.

   (i) Complete the diagram to show how the electrons are arranged in a sodium atom.

   (You may wish to use page 1 of the data booklet to help you.)

   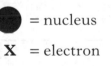
   ● = nucleus

   X = electron

   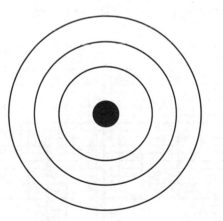

   1

   (ii) Explain what holds the negatively charged electrons in place around the nucleus.

   _____

   _____ 1

   (3)

Marks

2. The diagram shows the apparatus used to prepare chlorine gas. Concentrated hydrochloric acid is reacted with potassium permanganate. The gas produced is bubbled through water to remove any unreacted hydrochloric acid and is then dried by bubbling through concentrated sulphuric acid.

(*a*) Complete the diagram for the preparation of chlorine gas by adding the labels for concentrated sulphuric acid, potassium permanganate and water.

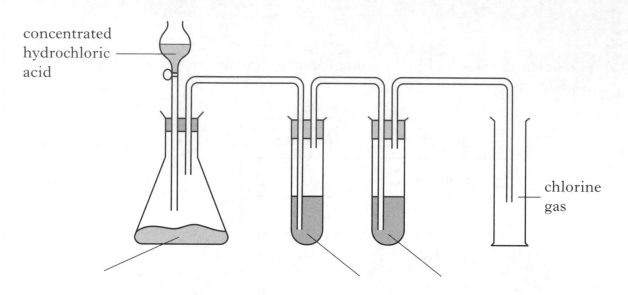

1

(*b*) Chlorine is a member of the Group 7 elements.

The graph shows the melting points of these elements.

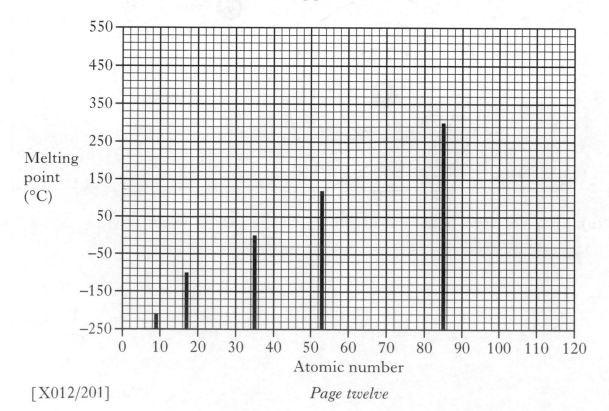

DO NOT WRITE IN THIS MARGIN

Marks

2. (*b*) (continued)

(i) State the relationship between the atomic number and the melting point of the Group 7 elements.

____

____

____ **1**

(ii) The next member of this group would have an atomic number of 117.

Using the graph, predict the melting point of this element.

Melting point ________________ °C **1**

(3)

[Turn over

Marks

3. When calcium chloride is dissolved in water, heat is released to the surroundings.

    (a) What term is used to describe chemical reactions which give out heat?

    _____ 1

    (b) A student investigated how changing the mass of calcium chloride affects the heat released.

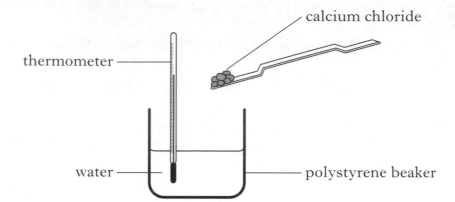

    The results are shown.

Mass of calcium chloride used (g)	Highest temperature reached (°C)
0	20
5	28
10	34
15	41
20	50
25	57

Marks

3. (*b*) **(continued)**

(i) Plot a line graph of these results.

(Additional graph paper, if required, can be found on page 30.)

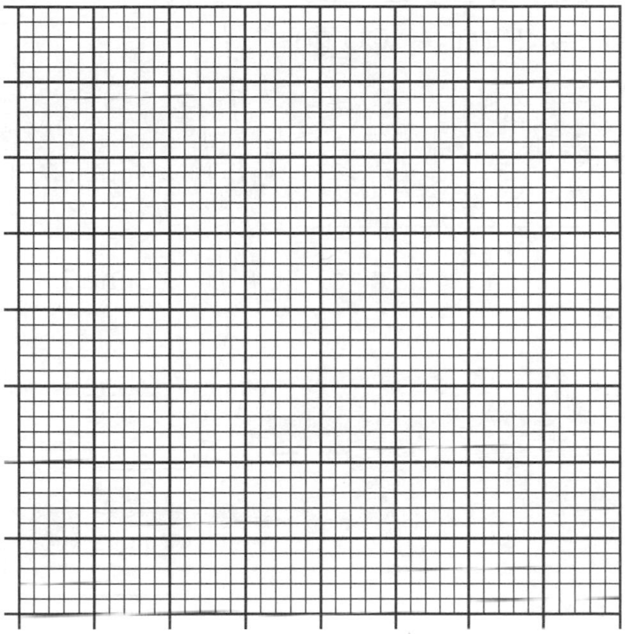

2

(ii) Using your graph, find the mass of calcium chloride that would give a temperature of 40 °C.

_____ g

1

(*c*) State an advantage of using a polystyrene beaker in this experiment.

_____

_____ 1

(5)

[Turn over

DO NOT
WRITE IN
THIS
MARGIN

Marks

4. Iron is produced from iron ore in a Blast Furnace.

iron ore, carbon
and limestone

Zone	Key reaction
3	$Fe_2O_3(s) + CO(g) \rightarrow Fe(\ell) + CO_2(g)$
2	$CO_2(g) + C(s) \rightarrow 2CO(g)$
1	$C(s) + O_2(g) \rightarrow CO_2(g)$

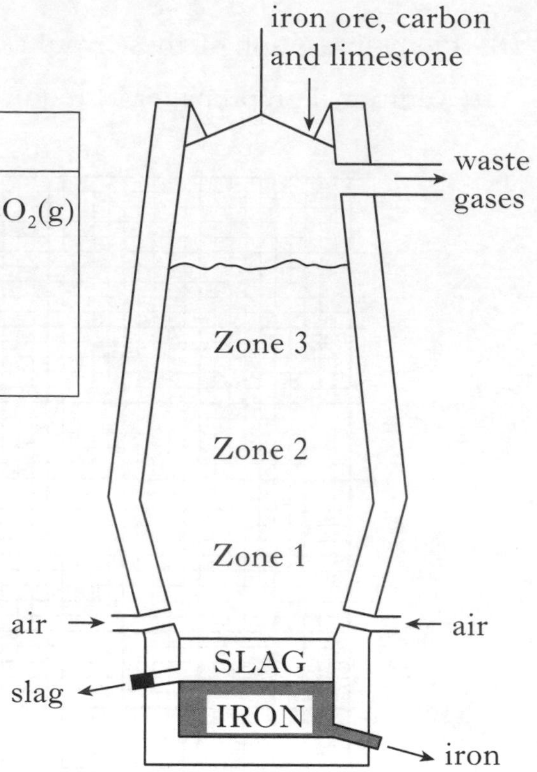

waste
gases

Zone 3

Zone 2

Zone 1

air →   ← air

slag ←

SLAG

IRON

→ iron

(a) The key reaction which takes place in Zone 3 is shown.

$$Fe_2O_3(s) + CO(g) \rightarrow Fe(\ell) + CO_2(g)$$

Balance this equation.   **1**

(b) The equation for the key reaction in Zone 2 is shown below. Calculate the mass of carbon monoxide produced when 1200 kg of carbon reacts.

$$CO_2(g) + C(s) \rightarrow 2CO(g)$$

_____ kg   **2**

(c) Why is air blown into the Blast Furnace?

_____   **1**

(4)

Marks

5. Air is a mixture of gases. These gases can be separated by the process of fractional distillation.

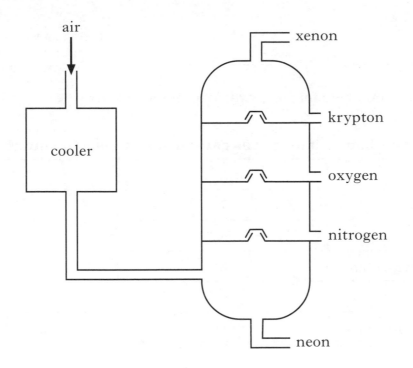

(a) Why can these gases be separated by fractional distillation?

_____

_____ 1

(b) Nitrogen is separated from the mixture at −200 °C.

Circle the state that nitrogen will be in at this temperature.

(You may wish to use page 3 of your data booklet to help you.)

solid   liquid   gas   1

(c) The cooler contains sodium hydroxide solution. This reacts with the carbon dioxide in the air and removes it from the mixture of gases.

Name the type of chemical reaction taking place.

_____ 1

(3)

[Turn over

Marks

6. The octane number of petrol is a measure of how efficiently it burns as a fuel. The higher the octane number, the more efficient the fuel.

(*a*) What is a fuel?

_____ 1

(*b*) The octane numbers for some hydrocarbons are shown.

Hydrocarbon	Number of carbon atoms	Octane number
hexane	6	
heptane	7	0
octane	8	−19
2-methylpentane	6	71
2-methylhexane	7	44
2-methylheptane	8	23

(i) Predict the octane number for hexane.

_____ 1

(ii) State a relationship between the structure of the hydrocarbon and their efficiency as fuels.

_____

_____

_____ 1

(3)

Marks

7. The diagram shows how paraffin, $C_{12}H_{26}$, can be cracked.

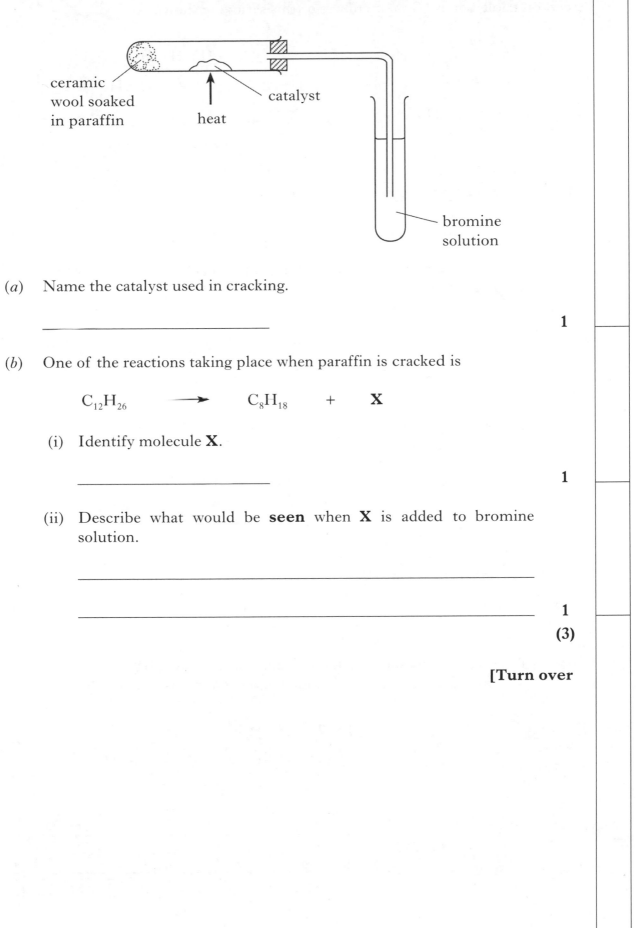

ceramic
wool soaked
in paraffin

heat

catalyst

bromine
solution

(a) Name the catalyst used in cracking.

_____

1

(b) One of the reactions taking place when paraffin is cracked is

$$C_{12}H_{26} \longrightarrow C_8H_{18} + \mathbf{X}$$

(i) Identify molecule **X**.

_____

1

(ii) Describe what would be **seen** when **X** is added to bromine
solution.

_____

_____

1

(3)

[Turn over

Marks

8. Alkynes are a homologous series of hydrocarbons which contain carbon to carbon triple bonds. Two members of this series are shown.

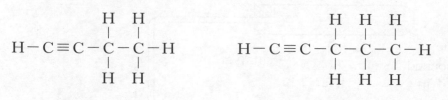

butyne   pentyne

(a) Name the first member of this series.

_____   **1**

(b) Alkynes can be prepared by reacting a dibromoalkane with potassium hydroxide solution.

$$H-\underset{\underset{Br}{|}}{\overset{\overset{H}{|}}{C}}-\underset{\underset{Br}{|}}{\overset{\overset{H}{|}}{C}}-\underset{\underset{H}{|}}{\overset{\overset{H}{|}}{C}}-H \; + \; 2KOH \; \rightarrow \; H-C\equiv C-\underset{\underset{H}{|}}{\overset{\overset{H}{|}}{C}}-H \; + \; 2KBr \; + \; H_2O$$

dibromoalkane   propyne

(i) Draw a structural formula for the alkyne formed when the dibromoalkane shown reacts with potassium hydroxide solution.

$$H-\underset{\underset{H}{|}}{\overset{\overset{H}{|}}{C}}-\underset{\underset{Br}{|}}{\overset{\overset{H}{|}}{C}}-\underset{\underset{Br}{|}}{\overset{\overset{H}{|}}{C}}-\underset{\underset{H}{|}}{\overset{\overset{H}{|}}{C}}-H \; + \; 2KOH \; \rightarrow$$

1

(ii) Suggest a reason why the dibromoalkane shown below does not form an alkyne when it is added to potassium hydroxide solution.

$$H-\underset{\underset{H}{|}}{\overset{\overset{H}{|}}{C}}-\underset{\underset{Br}{|}}{\overset{\overset{H}{|}}{C}}-\underset{\underset{H}{|}}{\overset{\overset{H}{|}}{C}}-\underset{\underset{Br}{|}}{\overset{\overset{H}{|}}{C}}-\underset{\underset{H}{|}}{\overset{\overset{H}{|}}{C}}-H$$

_____

_____   **1**

(3)

Marks

9. The enzyme RuBisCo is one of the most abundant enzymes on Earth. It contains lysine at its active site.

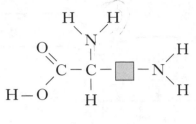

lysine

(a) Lysine contains two different types of functional groups.

Circle an amine group in the lysine molecule shown above.

1

(b) Name the family of compounds to which lysine belongs.

_____

1

(c) Complete the equation to show the structure of the other product formed when two molecules of lysine react.

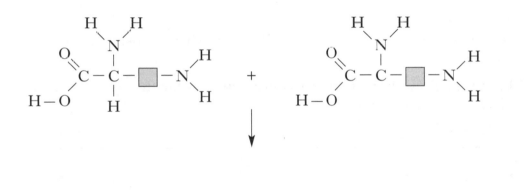

1

(3)

[Turn over

Marks

10. The flow chart shows some of the stages in the manufacture of ethanoic acid.

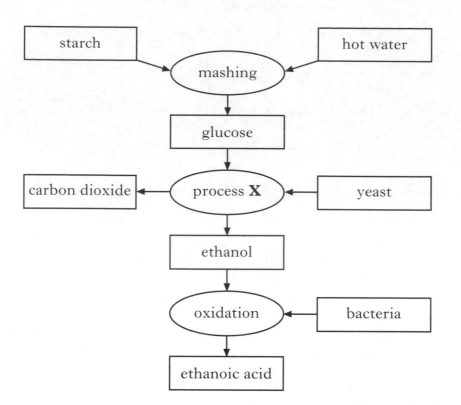

(a) In the mashing process, some of the starch is broken down into glucose.

Using the flow chart, write the word equation for the reaction taking place in the mashing process.

_____ 1

(b) Name process **X**.

_____ 1

(c) Draw the full structural formula for ethanoic acid.

1

(d) Ethanoic acid can be reacted with methanol to form an ester, which is used as a solvent in nail varnish remover.

Name this ester.

_____ 1

(4)

DO NOT
WRITE IN
THIS
MARGIN

Marks

11. Urea is a substance found in human urine. The enzyme urease catalyses the hydrolysis of urea. During the reaction, ammonia and carbon dioxide are produced.

$$NH_2CONH_2(aq) + H_2O(\ell) \longrightarrow 2NH_3(aq) + CO_2(g)$$

(a) What is an enzyme?

_____ 1

(b) The ammonia solution produced in this reaction is described as a weak base.

(i) What is meant by a weak base?

_____

_____ 1

(ii) The concentration of ammonia solution can be determined as follows:

1 pipette $10\,cm^3$ of ammonia solution into a conical flask
2 add 3 drops of indicator solution
3 add $0{\cdot}1\,mol\,l^{-1}$ of hydrochloric acid from a burette until the indicator changes colour

Name this technique.

_____ 1

(3)

[Turn over

Marks

12. Rhubarb contains oxalic acid, $C_2H_2O_4$. Oxalic acid decolourises acidified potassium permanganate solution.

An experiment was carried out to time how long it takes to decolourise the solution using different numbers of rhubarb cubes.

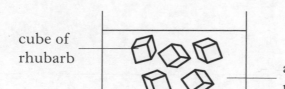

cube of rhubarb

acidified potassium permanganate solution

The results are shown.

Number of rhubarb cubes	Time to decolourise solution(s)	Relative rate (1/t) (s^{-1})
5	360	0·003
10		0·006
15	92	0·011
20	40	0·025

(a) Calculate the time taken for 10 cubes of rhubarb to decolourise the solution.

_____ s   **1**

(b) Using collision theory, explain why increasing the number of rhubarb cubes increases the rate of reaction.

_____

_____   **1**

DO NOT WRITE IN THIS MARGIN

Marks

12. (continued)

(*c*) The equation for the reaction between permanganate solution and the oxalic acid in rhubarb is

$$2MnO_4^- + 5C_2H_2O_4 + 6H^+ \longrightarrow 2Mn^{2+} + 10CO_2 + 8H_2O.$$

2 moles 5 moles

(i) Calculate the number of moles of permanganate ions (MnO_4^-) in 100 cm^3 of a 1·0 mol l^{-1} solution.

____________ mol **1**

(ii) The above equation shows that 2 moles of permanganate ions react with 5 moles of oxalic acid.

How many moles of oxalic acid ($C_2H_2O_4$) react with 100 cm^3 of 1·0 mol l^{-1} permanganate (MnO_4^-) solution?

____________ mol **1**

(4)

[Turn over

Marks

13. Part of a student's PPA sheet is shown.

Intermediate 2 Chemistry	Preparation of a Salt	Unit 3 PPA1

Aim

The aim of this experiment is to make a magnesium salt by the reaction of magnesium/magnesium carbonate with sulphuric acid.

Procedure

1. Using a measuring cylinder add 20 cm^3 of dilute acid to the beaker.

2. Add a spatulaful of magnesium or magnesium carbonate to the acid and stir the reaction mixture with a glass rod.

3. If all the solid reacts add another spatulaful of magnesium or magnesium carbonate and stir the mixture.

4. Continue adding the magnesium or magnesium carbonate until . . .

(a) Complete the instruction for step 4 of the procedure.

_____

_____

_____   1

(b) Why is an excess of magnesium or magnesium carbonate added to the acid?

_____

_____

_____   1

(c) The equation for the preparation of magnesium sulphate from magnesium carbonate is shown.

$$MgCO_3(s) + H_2SO_4(aq) \rightarrow MgSO_4(aq) + \underline{\hspace{1.5cm}} + \underline{\hspace{1.5cm}}$$

Complete the equation showing the formulae for the missing products.   1

(3)

Marks

14.   When iron reacts with water and oxygen, rust forms.

The chemical name for rust is iron(III) oxide.

(a) Write the chemical formula for rust.

_____   1

(b) During rusting, iron initially loses 2 electrons to form iron(II) ions. These are further oxidised to form iron(III) ions.

Write the ion-electron equation to show iron(II) ions forming iron(III) ions.

(You may wish to use page 7 of the data booklet to help you.)

_____   1

(c) Some iron railings were fixed into stone walls by using plugs of lead. Over time, the iron railings rusted faster at the point of contact with the lead.

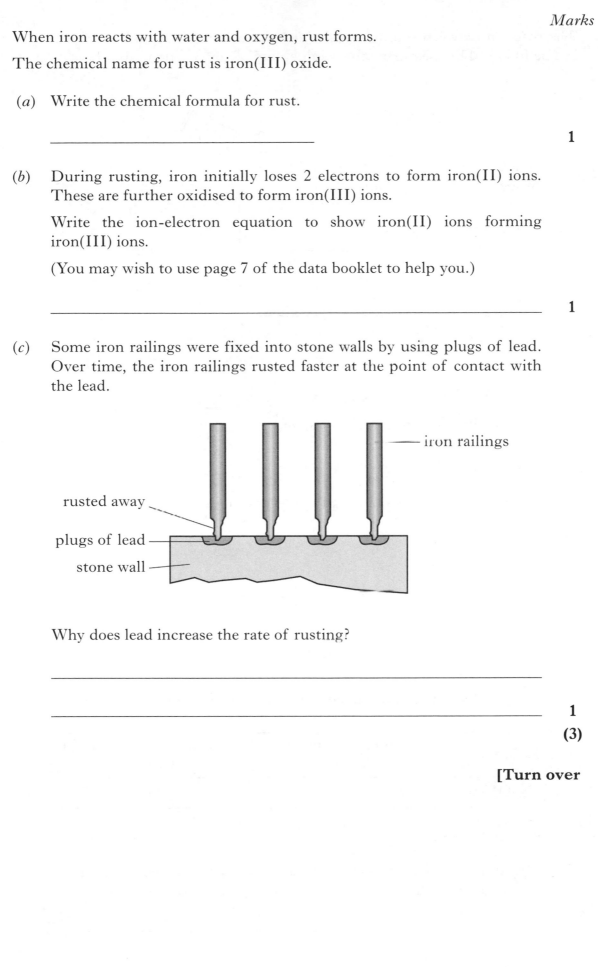

Why does lead increase the rate of rusting?

_____

_____   1
                                                          (3)

[Turn over

Marks

15. The reaction between sodium hydroxide solution and dilute sulphuric acid can be followed by measuring the conductivity of the reaction mixture.

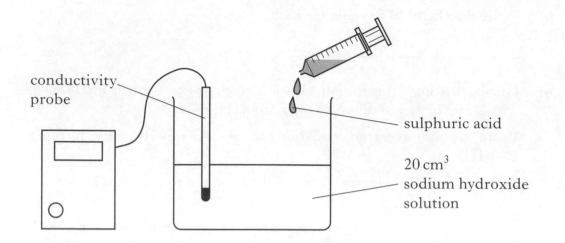

The conductivity probe measures the conductivity of the solution as the reaction proceeds.

(*a*)   The equation for the reaction is shown.

$$2Na^+(aq) + 2OH^-(aq) + 2H^+(aq) + SO_4^{2-}(aq) \longrightarrow 2Na^+(aq) + SO_4^{2-}(aq) + 2H_2O(\ell)$$

Rewrite the equation omitting the spectator ions.

1

(*b*)   The experiment was repeated using $20\,cm^3$ barium hydroxide solution.

The results of both experiments are shown in the table.

Solution	Conductivity at start (mA)	Conductivity at end-point (mA)
$0\cdot1\,mol\,l^{-1}\ NaOH(aq)$	80	35
$0\cdot1\,mol\,l^{-1}\ Ba(OH)_2(aq)$	160	0

(i)   Why does barium hydroxide solution have a higher conductivity than the sodium hydroxide solution at the start?

_____

_____ 1

Marks

15. (*b*) **(continued)**

The equation for the reaction between barium hydroxide solution and sulphuric acid is shown.

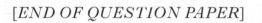

$$Ba^{2+}(aq) + 2OH^-(aq) + 2H^+(aq) + SO_4{}^{2-}(aq) \longrightarrow Ba^{2+}SO_4{}^{2-}(s) + 2H_2O(\ell)$$

(ii) Why is the conductivity reading at the end point 0 mA?

_____

_____

1

(3)

[*END OF QUESTION PAPER*]

ADDITIONAL SPACE FOR ANSWERS

ADDITIONAL GRAPH PAPER FOR QUESTION 3(*b*)(i)

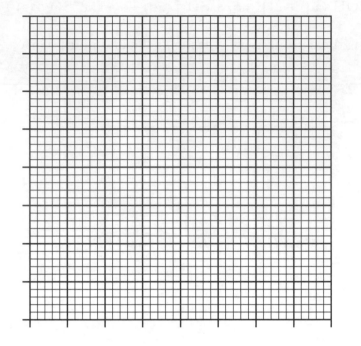

ADDITIONAL SPACE FOR ANSWERS

[BLANK PAGE]

[BLANK PAGE]

FOR OFFICIAL USE

Section B   Total Marks

X012/201

| NATIONAL QUALIFICATIONS 2010 | WEDNESDAY, 2 JUNE 9.00 AM – 11.00 AM | CHEMISTRY INTERMEDIATE 2 |

Fill in these boxes and read what is printed below.

Full name of centre

Town

Forename(s)

Surname

Date of birth

Day   Month   Year   Scottish candidate number   Number of seat

Necessary data will be found in the Chemistry Data Booklet for Standard Grade and Intermediate 2.

Section A   Questions 1 30 (30 marks)

Instructions for completion of **Section A** are given on page two.

For this section of the examination you must use an **HB pencil**.

Section B (50 marks)

All questions should be attempted.

The questions may be answered in any order but all answers are to be written in the spaces provided in this answer book, **and must be written clearly and legibly in ink**.

Rough work, if any should be necessary, should be written in this book, and then scored through when the fair copy has been written. If further space is required, a supplementary sheet for rough work may be obtained from the Invigilator.

Additional space for answers will be found at the end of the book. If further space is required, supplementary sheets may be obtained from the Invigilator and should be inserted inside the **front** cover of this booklet.

Before leaving the examination room you must give this book to the Invigilator. If you do not, you may lose all the marks for this paper.

Read carefully

1 Check that the answer sheet provided is for **Chemistry Intermediate 2 (Section A)**.

2 For this section of the examination you must use an **HB pencil** and, where necessary, an eraser.

3 Check that the answer sheet you have been given has **your name**, **date of birth**, **SCN** (Scottish Candidate Number) and **Centre Name** printed on it.

   Do not change any of these details.

4 If any of this information is wrong, tell the Invigilator immediately.

5 If this information is correct, **print** your name and seat number in the boxes provided.

6 The answer to each question is **either** A, B, C or D. Decide what your answer is, then, using your pencil, put a horizontal line in the space provided (see sample question below).

7 There is **only one correct** answer to each question.

8 Any rough working should be done on the question paper or the rough working sheet, **not** on your answer sheet.

9 At the end of the examination, put the **answer sheet for Section A inside the front cover of this answer book**.

Sample Question

To show that the ink in a ball-pen consists of a mixture of dyes, the method of separation would be

       A chromatography

       B fractional distillation

       C fractional crystallisation

       D filtration.

The correct answer is **A**—chromatography. The answer **A** has been clearly marked in **pencil** with a horizontal line (see below).

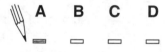

Changing an answer

If you decide to change your answer, carefully erase your first answer and using your pencil, fill in the answer you want. The answer below has been changed to **D**.

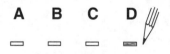

SECTION A

1. Which of the following changes is **not** an example of a chemical reaction?

    A Ice melting

    B Iron rusting

    C Methane burning

    D Neutralising an acid

2. During the first 20 seconds of a chemical reaction, $5.0 \, cm^3$ of gas were given off.

    The average rate of the reaction, in $cm^3 \, s^{-1}$, during the first 20 seconds is

    A 20·0

    B 5·0

    C 4·0

    D 0·25.

3. Some of the bonds in an amino acid molecule are polar covalent.

    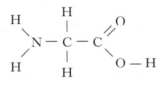

    The table contains information about the attraction of some atoms for bonded electrons.

Atom	Relative attraction for bonded electrons
H	2·2
C	2·5
N	3·0
O	3·5

    The most polar bond in the amino acid molecule will be

    A C — H

    B N — H

    C O — H

    D C — O.

4. Metallic bonds are due to

    A pairs of electrons being shared equally between atoms

    B pairs of electrons being shared unequally between atoms

    C the attraction of oppositely charged ions for each other

    D the attraction of positively charged ions for delocalised electrons.

5. Which of the following elements exists as diatomic molecules?

    A Carbon

    B Helium

    C Nitrogen

    D Sulphur

6. A solution containing chloride ions, fluoride ions and bromide ions was electrolysed.

    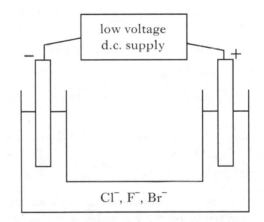

    The speed at which ions move towards an electrode depends on the size of the ion.

    The bigger the ion the slower it moves.

    The order in which the negative ions would reach the positive electrode, from first to last, is

    A Br^-, Cl^-, F^-

    B Br^-, F^-, Cl^-

    C F^-, Br^-, Cl^-

    D F^-, Cl^-, Br^-.

[Turn over

7. The formula for magnesium sulphite is

   A MgS

   B $MgSO_3$

   C $MgSO_4$

   D MgS_2O_3.

8. $xAl(s) + yBr_2(\ell) \rightarrow zAlBr_3(s)$

   This equation will be balanced when

   A $x = 1, y = 2, z = 1$

   B $x = 2, y = 3, z = 2$

   C $x = 3, y = 2, z = 3$

   D $x = 4, y = 3, z = 4$.

9. The isotopes of carbon and oxygen are given in the table.

Isotopes of carbon	$^{12}_{6}C$	$^{13}_{6}C$	$^{14}_{6}C$
Isotopes of oxygen	$^{16}_{8}O$	$^{17}_{8}O$	$^{18}_{8}O$

   A molecule of carbon dioxide with mass 46 could contain

   A   one ^{12}C atom and two ^{16}O atoms

   B   one ^{14}C atom and two ^{18}O atoms

   C   one ^{12}C atom, one ^{16}O atom and one ^{18}O atom

   D   one ^{14}C atom, one ^{16}O atom and one ^{18}O atom.

10. 1 mole of a hydrocarbon burns completely in oxygen to produce 2 moles of carbon dioxide and 2 moles of water.

    The formula for the hydrocarbon is

    A C_2H_4

    B C_2H_6

    C C_4H_8

    D C_4H_{10}.

11. The properties of fractions obtained from crude oil depend on the sizes of molecules in the fractions.

    Compared with a fraction containing small molecules, a fraction containing large molecules will

    A   be more viscous

    B   be more flammable

    C   evaporate more readily

    D   have a lower boiling point range.

12. Which of the following hydrocarbons does **not** belong to the same homologous series as the others?

    A CH_4

    B C_3H_8

    C C_4H_{10}

    D C_6H_{12}

13. Which type of reaction is shown by the following equation?

$$H-\underset{\underset{H}{|}}{\overset{\overset{H}{|}}{C}}-\underset{\underset{H}{|}}{\overset{\overset{H}{|}}{C}}-\underset{\underset{OH}{|}}{\overset{\overset{H}{|}}{C}}-H \rightarrow H-\underset{\underset{H}{|}}{\overset{\overset{H}{|}}{C}}-\underset{\overset{H}{|}}{C}=\overset{\overset{H}{|}}{C}-H + H_2O$$

    A   Condensation

    B   Dehydration

    C   Hydration

    D   Hydrolysis

14. Which of the following polymers dissolves in water?

    A   Kevlar

    B   Perspex

    C   Poly(ethene)

    D   Poly(ethenol)

15. The structure below shows a section of an addition polymer.

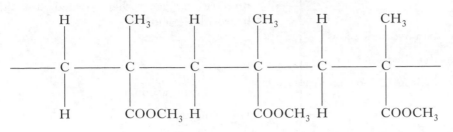

Which molecule is used to make this polymer?

A
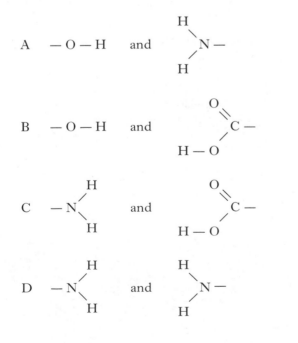

B

C

D

---

16. Which of the following groups can react together to form an amide (peptide) link?

A $-O-H$ and $\overset{H}{\underset{H}{\diagdown}}N-$

B $-O-H$ and $\underset{H-O}{\overset{O}{\diagdown}}C-$

C $-N\overset{H}{\underset{H}{\diagdown}}$ and $\underset{H-O}{\overset{O}{\diagdown}}C-$

D $-N\overset{H}{\underset{H}{\diagdown}}$ and $\overset{H}{\underset{H}{\diagdown}}N-$

17. When a reversible reaction is at equilibrium, the concentrations of reactants and products are

A   constant but not equal

B   constant and equal

C   not constant but equal

D   not constant and not equal.

18. Which of the following substances dissolves in water to give a solution of pH greater than 7?

A   Ammonia

B   Carbon dioxide

C   Sulphur dioxide

D   Sodium chloride

[Turn over

19. An acidic solution contains

    A   only hydrogen ions

    B   more hydrogen ions than hydroxide ions

    C   more hydroxide ions than hydrogen ions

    D   equal numbers of hydrogen ions and hydroxide ions.

20. What mass of ammonium sulphate, $(NH_4)_2SO_4$, is required to produce 0·5 litres of a $1\ mol\,l^{-1}$ solution?

    A   32 g

    B   64 g

    C   66 g

    D   132 g

21. Which line in the table correctly shows the properties of $0·1\ mol\,l^{-1}$ hydrochloric acid when compared with $0·1\ mol\,l^{-1}$ ethanoic acid?

	pH	Conductivity	Rate of reaction with magnesium
A	lower	lower	slower
B	higher	higher	faster
C	lower	higher	faster
D	higher	lower	slower

22. Which of the following potassium compounds is a base?

    A   Potassium nitrate

    B   Potassium chloride

    C   Potassium sulphate

    D   Potassium carbonate

23. In a neutralisation reaction between an acid and an alkali, the pH

    A   of the acid increases

    B   of the acid is unchanged

    C   of the alkali increases

    D   of the alkali is unchanged.

24. Which of the following substances will **not** produce a gas when added to dilute hydrochloric acid?

    A   Copper

    B   Zinc

    C   Copper carbonate

    D   Zinc carbonate

25. Which salt can **not** be prepared by a precipitation reaction?

    (You may wish to use the data booklet to help you.)

    A   Barium sulphate

    B   Lead(II) sulphate

    C   Calcium chloride

    D   Silver chloride

26. The equation for the reaction between lead(II) nitrate and sodium iodide is:

$$Pb^{2+}(aq) + 2NO_3^{-}(aq) + 2Na^{+}(aq) + 2I^{-}(aq)$$
$$\downarrow$$
$$Pb^{2+}(I^{-})_2(s) + 2Na^{+}(aq) + 2NO_3^{-}(aq)$$

    The spectator ions present in this reaction are

    A $Na^{+}(aq)$ and $NO_3^{-}(aq)$

    B $Na^{+}(aq)$ and $I^{-}(aq)$

    C $Pb^{2+}(aq)$ and $NO_3^{-}(aq)$

    D $Pb^{2+}(aq)$ and $I^{-}(aq)$.

27. Which metal will displace zinc from a solution of zinc sulphate?

    A   Iron

    B   Magnesium

    C   Silver

    D   Tin

28. The ion-electron equation for the oxidation and reduction steps in the reaction between magnesium and silver(I) ions are:

$$Mg \rightarrow Mg^{2+} + 2e^-$$
$$Ag^+ + e^- \rightarrow Ag$$

The overall redox equation is

A $Mg + 2Ag^+ \rightarrow Mg^{2+} + 2Ag$

B $Mg + Ag^+ \rightarrow Mg^{2+} + Ag$

C $Mg + Ag^+ + e^- \rightarrow Mg^{2+} + Ag + 2e^-$

D $Mg + 2Ag \rightarrow Mg^{2+} + 2Ag^+.$

29. Aluminium can be extracted from aluminium oxide by

A heating alone

B heating with carbon

C heating with carbon monoxide

D electrolysis.

30. An iron nail is covered with water.

Which of the following would increase the rate at which the iron nail rusts?

A Adding glucose to the water

B Wrapping magnesium around the nail

C Adding potassium nitrate to the water

D Attaching the nail to the negative terminal of a d.c. power supply

Candidates are reminded that the answer sheet for Section A MUST be placed INSIDE the front cover of this answer book.

[Turn over

[BLANK PAGE]

Marks

SECTION B

50 marks are available in this section of the paper.

All answers must be written clearly and legibly in ink.

1. Elements are made up of atoms.

   An atom of an element is represented by the diagram below.

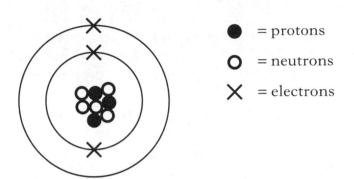

   ● = protons

   ○ = neutrons

   ✕ = electrons

   (a) What name is given to the part of the atom which contains protons and neutrons?

   _____   1

   (b) Using the information in the diagram:

      (i) state the mass number of this atom;

      _____   1

      (ii) explain why this atom is electrically neutral;

      _____

      _____   1

      (iii) name the **family** of elements to which this atom belongs.

      _____   1

                                                                 (4)

   [Turn over

Marks

2. Cool packs can be used to treat some sports injuries.

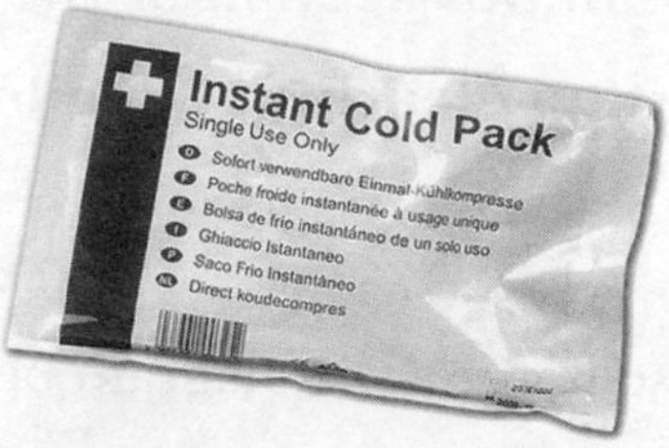

The pack contains solid ammonium nitrate and water in two separate compartments. When the pack is squeezed the ammonium nitrate dissolves in the water forming a solution. This results in a drop in temperature.

(a) What term is used to describe a reaction in which there is a drop in temperature?

_____   1

(b) The equation for the reaction taking place in the cool pack is shown.

$$NH_4NO_3(\quad) + H_2O(\quad) \rightarrow NH_4NO_3(\quad)$$

Complete the equation by adding state symbols.   1

(c) What name is given to a liquid, such as water, that can be used to dissolve substances?

_____   1

(d) The change in temperature in the cool pack can be calculated using the equation below.

$$\text{Temperature change} = \frac{\text{energy change (kJ)}}{\text{mass of water (kg)} \times 4\cdot2}$$

Calculate the temperature change using the following information.

Energy change (kJ)	6·72
Mass of water (kg)	0·2

_____ °C   1

(4)

Marks

3. The element carbon can exist in the form of diamond.

The structure of diamond is shown in the diagram.

(a) Name the type of **bonding** and **structure** present in diamond.

_____   1

(b) Carbon forms many compounds with other elements such as hydrogen.

(i) Draw a diagram to show how the outer electrons are arranged in a molecule of methane, CH_4.

1

(ii) Draw a diagram to show the **shape** of a molecule of methane, CH_4.

1

(3)

4. Gold is a very soft metal. In order to make it harder, goldsmiths mix it with silver. The quality of the gold is indicated in carats.

(*a*) The graph shows information about the quality of gold.

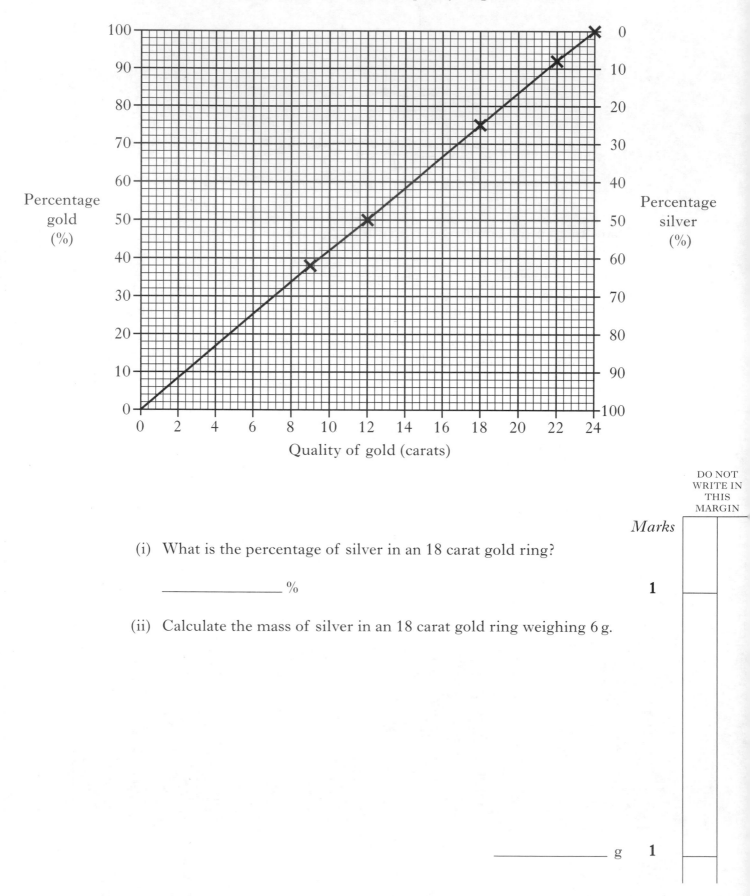

Quality of gold (carats)

Marks

(i) What is the percentage of silver in an 18 carat gold ring?

_____ %

1

(ii) Calculate the mass of silver in an 18 carat gold ring weighing 6 g.

_____ g

1

DO NOT WRITE IN THIS MARGIN

Marks

4. (continued)

(*b*) Silver tarnishes in air forming black silver sulphide, Ag_2S.

The equation for the reaction is:

$$4Ag + 2H_2S + O_2 \longrightarrow 2Ag_2S + 2H_2O$$

What mass of silver sulphide would be formed from 1·08 g of silver? **2**

(4)

[Turn over

Marks

5. The diagram below shows the apparatus used in the **PPA**, **"Cracking"**.

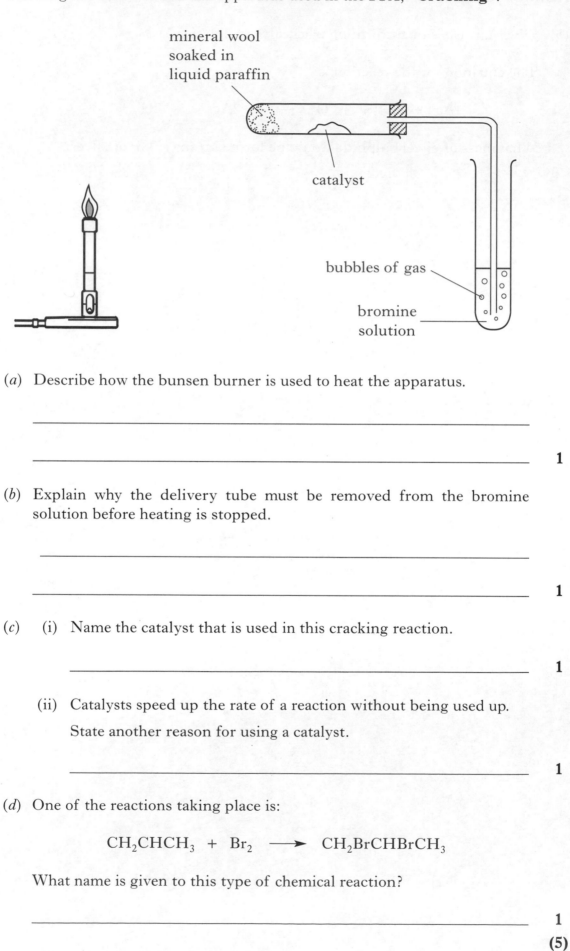

mineral wool
soaked in
liquid paraffin

catalyst

bubbles of gas

bromine
solution

(*a*) Describe how the bunsen burner is used to heat the apparatus.

_____

_____   1

(*b*) Explain why the delivery tube must be removed from the bromine solution before heating is stopped.

_____

_____   1

(*c*) (i) Name the catalyst that is used in this cracking reaction.

_____   1

(ii) Catalysts speed up the rate of a reaction without being used up.

State another reason for using a catalyst.

_____   1

(*d*) One of the reactions taking place is:

$$CH_2CHCH_3 \ + \ Br_2 \ \longrightarrow \ CH_2BrCHBrCH_3$$

What name is given to this type of chemical reaction?

_____   1

(5)

Marks

6. Chemicals in food provide flavour and smell. Ketones are responsible for the flavour in blue cheese.

Two examples of ketones are shown below.

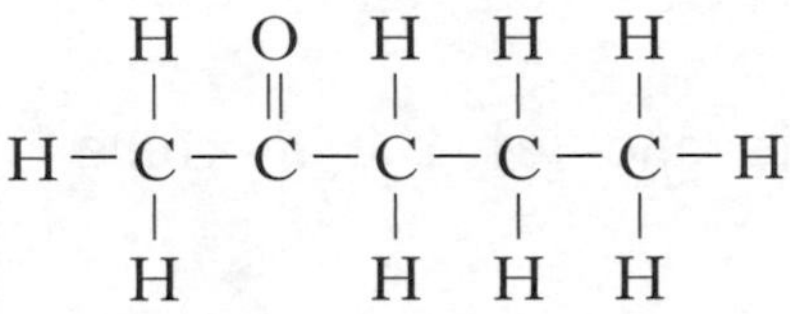

$$
\begin{array}{ccccc}
\text{H} & \text{O} & \text{H} & \text{H} & \text{H} \\
| & || & | & | & | \\
\text{H}-\text{C}-\text{C}-\text{C}-\text{C}-\text{C}-\text{H} \\
| & & | & | & | \\
\text{H} & & \text{H} & \text{H} & \text{H}
\end{array}
\qquad
\begin{array}{ccccc}
\text{H} & \text{H} & \text{O} & \text{H} & \text{H} \\
| & | & || & | & | \\
\text{H}-\text{C}-\text{C}-\text{C}-\text{C}-\text{C}-\text{H} \\
| & | & & | & | \\
\text{H} & \text{H} & & \text{H} & \text{H}
\end{array}
$$

pentan-2-one 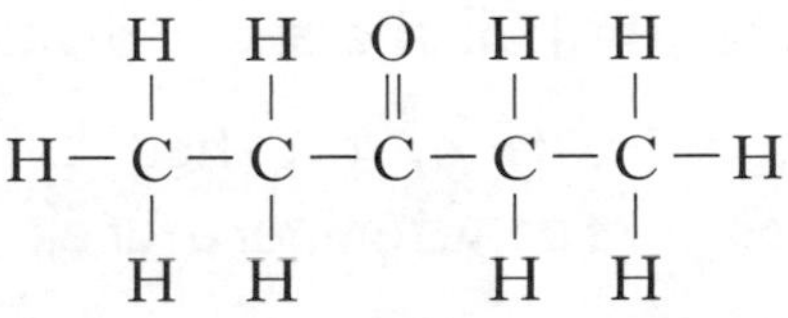   pentan-3-one

(a) Draw a structure for hexan-3-one.

1

(b) Suggest a name for the ketone shown below.

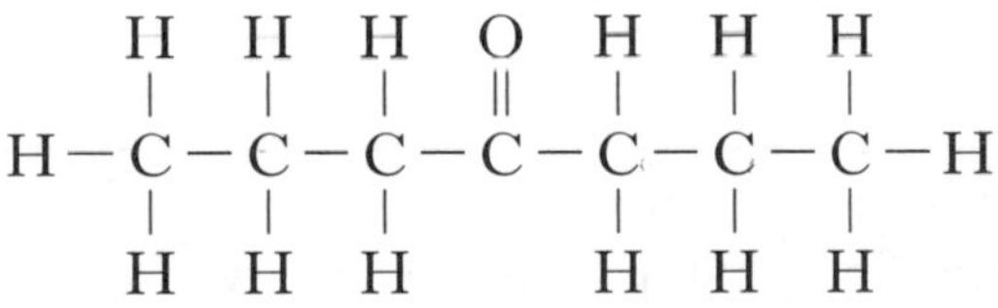

$$
\begin{array}{ccccccc}
\text{H} & \text{H} & \text{H} & \text{O} & \text{H} & \text{H} & \text{H} \\
| & | & | & || & | & | & | \\
\text{H}-\text{C}-\text{C}-\text{C}-\text{C}-\text{C}-\text{C}-\text{C}-\text{H} \\
| & | & | & & | & | & | \\
\text{H} & \text{H} & \text{H} & & \text{H} & \text{H} & \text{H}
\end{array}
$$

_____ 1

(c) Information about the boiling points of four ketones is shown in the table.

Ketone	Boiling point (°C)
C_3H_6O	56
C_4H_8O	80
$C_5H_{10}O$	102
$C_6H_{12}O$	127

Predict the boiling point of $C_7H_{14}O$.

_____ °C   1

(3)

[Turn over

Marks

7. A recipe for making blackcurrant wine is shown.

1. Boil 4 litres of water and add 2 kg of sugar.
2. Stir until all the sugar dissolves.
3. Add 1·5 kg of crushed blackcurrants and let the mixture cool to room temperature.
4. Add some yeast.
5. Cover the container and leave it in a warm place for 5 days.
6. Filter the mixture into a glass jar and fit an airlock.
7. Leave the mixture for 3 months before filtering and bottling.

(*a*) Yeast is used to convert sugar into ethanol.

(i) What name is given to this process?

_____ 1

(ii) What **type** of substance, found in yeast, acts as a catalyst?

_____ 1

(*b*) Why was the mixture cooled at step 3, before the yeast was added to it?

_____

_____ 1

(*c*) When blackcurrant brandy is made from blackcurrant wine, the ethanol concentration is increased.

How could this be done?

_____ 1

(4)

DO NOT WRITE IN THIS MARGIN

Marks

8. Sweets, such as pineapple cubes, contain the artificial flavouring methyl butanoate.

(*a*) To which family of compounds does methyl butanoate belong?

________________________________ **1**

(*b*) Methyl butanoate can be broken down to form an alkanol and an alkanoic acid.

(i) Name this type of chemical reaction.

________________________________ **1**

(ii) Draw the full structural formula for the alkanoic acid formed from the breakdown of methyl butanoate. **1**

(3)

[Turn over

Marks

9.

Autumn days

Adapted from an article by Victoria Ashton

September 2001

The leaves of a Beech tree contain three coloured pigments; chlorophyll which is green, carotenes which are yellow and tannins which are brown.

In summer, the leaves are green as they contain a lot of chlorophyll. The chlorophyll is involved in converting water and carbon dioxide into glucose and oxygen. The glucose formed can then be converted into starch by condensation polymerisation.

In autumn the chlorophyll is broken down, supplying the tree with essential magnesium ions (Mg^{2+}) which it will need over the winter. As a result, the colours of the carotenes and tannins dominate in autumn, giving the Beech tree its golden yellow coloured leaves.

(a) What name is given to the process, in which water and carbon dioxide are converted into glucose and oxygen?

_____   1

(b) State a test and the result that you would get, which would distinguish between glucose and starch.

_____

_____   1

(c) The structure of a tannin molecule is shown below.

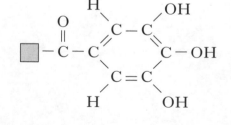

$\boxed{}$ (Circle) a hydroxyl group in this structure.   1

(d) What is the electron arrangement for a magnesium ion, Mg^{2+}?

_____   1

(4)

DO NOT
WRITE IN
THIS
MARGIN

Marks

10. People often drink lemonade to quench their thirst.

(a) Lemonade contains citric acid.

Suggest a pH value for lemonade.

_____   1

(b) To make the drink fizzy, carbon dioxide gas is added to the lemonade. The solubility of carbon dioxide gas depends on the temperature of the lemonade.

The graph shows how the solubility of carbon dioxide gas changes with temperature.

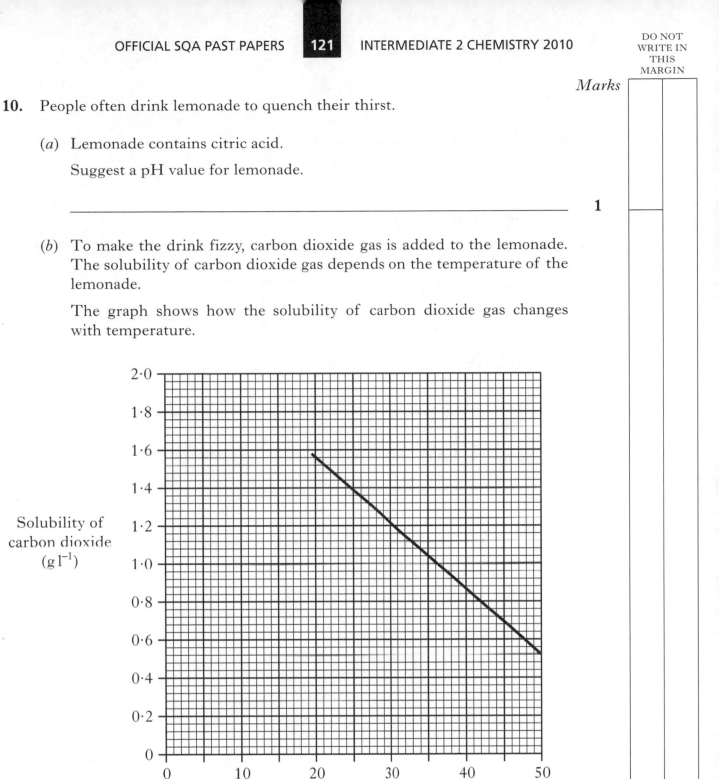

(i) Write a general statement describing the effect of temperature on the solubility of carbon dioxide gas.

_____

_____   1

(ii) Use the graph to predict the solubility of carbon dioxide at 10 °C.

_____ $g\,l^{-1}$ 1

     (3)

Marks

11.   Slaked lime can be added to lochs to reduce acidity.

     (*a*)   What causes the lochs to become acidic?

     _____   1

     (*b*)   Slaked lime can be made from limestone.

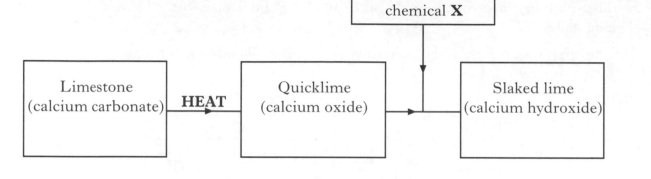

         (i)   Name the elements present in calcium carbonate.

         _____   1

         (ii)   Suggest a name for chemical **X**.

         _____   1

                                                                          (3)

Marks

12. Lamp posts made of iron or steel can have different coatings to prevent rusting.

(*a*) Some lamp posts are coated in a layer of paint.

How does the layer of paint prevent the iron lamp post from rusting?

_____

_____ 1

(*b*) Lamp posts can also be coated by dipping them in molten zinc.

   (i) What term is used to describe this process?

_____ 1

   (ii) Why does the iron not rust even when the zinc coating is scratched?

_____

_____ 1

                                                                      (3)

[Turn over

Marks

13. Sodium sulphate crystals can be made from sodium hydroxide solution and dilute sulphuric acid as shown in the procedure below.

Step 1

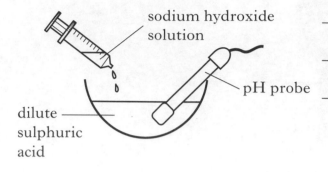

sodium hydroxide
solution

pH probe

dilute
sulphuric
acid

Add sodium hydroxide solution to dilute sulphuric acid until

_____

_____

_____

Step 2

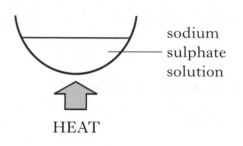

sodium
sulphate
solution

HEAT

Evaporate until half of the solution remains.

Step 3

sodium
sulphate
solution

Leave until the remaining water evaporates.

Step 4

sodium
sulphate
crystals

Sodium sulphate crystals are formed.

(a) Complete the instructions for Step 1.

1

DO NOT WRITE IN THIS MARGIN

Marks

13. (continued)

(*b*) The equation for the reaction is:

$$H_2SO_4 \quad + \quad 2NaOH \longrightarrow Na_2SO_4 \quad + \quad 2H_2O$$

In the experiment 50 cm^3 of sodium hydroxide solution reacted with 20 cm^3 0·1 mol l^{-1} dilute sulphuric acid.

Calculate the concentration of the sodium hydroxide solution.

____________ mol l^{-1} **2**

(3)

[Turn over

Marks

14. (*a*) In a **PPA**, a student was asked to investigate if the type of electrolyte used affects the voltage produced in a cell.

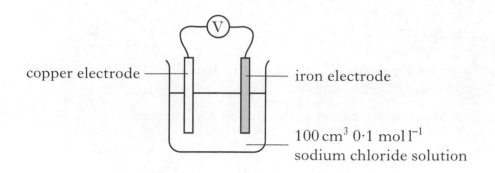

copper electrode — iron electrode

$100\,cm^3$ $0\cdot1\,mol\,l^{-1}$ sodium chloride solution

(i) Complete the labelling of a second cell which could be used to compare the effect of changing the electrolyte from sodium chloride to hydrochloric acid.

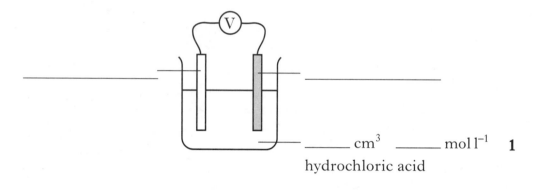

_____ cm^3 _____ $mol\,l^{-1}$ **1**

hydrochloric acid

(ii) What is done during this PPA to make sure the results are reliable?

_____   **1**

Marks

14.   **(continued)**

(*b*) Cells can also be made in which both metals and non-metals are used.

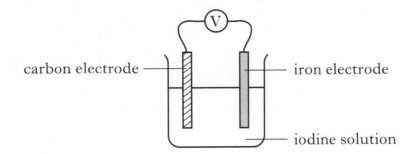

(i) The ion-electron equation for the reaction taking place at the carbon electrode is:

$$I_2(aq) \quad + \quad 2e^- \quad \longrightarrow \quad 2I^-(aq)$$

On the diagram clearly mark the path and direction of electron flow.

1

(ii) What property of carbon makes it suitable for use as an electrode?

_____

1

(4)

[END OF QUESTION PAPER]

DO NOT
WRITE IN
THIS
MARGIN

ADDITIONAL SPACE FOR ANSWERS

2011

[BLANK PAGE]

FOR OFFICIAL USE

Section B   Total Marks

X012/201

NATIONAL QUALIFICATIONS 2011

THURSDAY, 26 MAY 1.00 PM – 3.00 PM

CHEMISTRY INTERMEDIATE 2

Fill in these boxes and read what is printed below.

Full name of centre

Town

Forename(s)

Surname

Date of birth

Day   Month   Year   Scottish candidate number   Number of seat

Necessary data will be found in the Chemistry Data Booklet for Standard Grade and Intermediate 2.

Section A – Questions 1–30 (30 marks)

Instructions for completion of **Section A** are given on page two.

For this section of the examination you must use an **HB pencil**.

Section B (50 marks)

All questions should be attempted.

The questions may be answered in any order but all answers are to be written in the spaces provided in this answer book, **and must be written clearly and legibly in ink**.

Rough work, if any should be necessary, should be written in this book, and then scored through when the fair copy has been written. If further space is required, a supplementary sheet for rough work may be obtained from the Invigilator.

Additional space for answers will be found at the end of the book. If further space is required, supplementary sheets may be obtained from the Invigilator and should be inserted inside the **front** cover of this booklet.

Before leaving the examination room you must give this book to the Invigilator. If you do not, you may lose all the marks for this paper.

Read carefully

1   Check that the answer sheet provided is for **Chemistry Intermediate 2 (Section A)**.

2   For this section of the examination you must use an **HB pencil** and, where necessary, an eraser.

3   Check that the answer sheet you have been given has **your name**, **date of birth**, **SCN** (Scottish Candidate Number) and **Centre Name** printed on it.

    Do not change any of these details.

4   If any of this information is wrong, tell the Invigilator immediately.

5   If this information is correct, **print** your name and seat number in the boxes provided.

6   The answer to each question is **either** A, B, C or D. Decide what your answer is, then, using your pencil, put a horizontal line in the space provided (see sample question below).

7   There is **only one correct** answer to each question.

8   Any rough working should be done on the question paper or the rough working sheet, **not** on your answer sheet.

9   At the end of the examination, put the **answer sheet for Section A inside the front cover of this answer book**.

Sample Question

To show that the ink in a ball-pen consists of a mixture of dyes, the method of separation would be

    A   chromatography

    B   fractional distillation

    C   fractional crystallisation

    D   filtration.

The correct answer is **A**—chromatography. The answer **A** has been clearly marked in **pencil** with a horizontal line (see below).

Changing an answer

If you decide to change your answer, carefully erase your first answer and using your pencil, fill in the answer you want. The answer below has been changed to **D**.

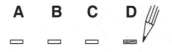

SECTION A

1. Which of the following compounds contains both a transition metal ion and a halide ion?

   A   Aluminium bromide

   B   Cobalt chloride

   C   Iron oxide

   D   Sodium fluoride

2. Which of the following compounds contains only two elements?

   A   Magnesium hydroxide

   B   Magnesium phosphate

   C   Magnesium sulphite

   D   Magnesium nitride

3. A student investigated the reaction between marble chips and excess dilute hydrochloric acid.

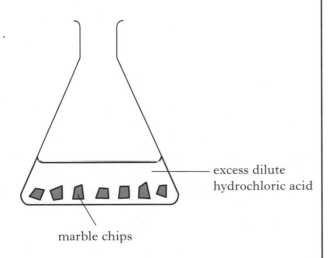

   — excess dilute hydrochloric acid

   marble chips

   Which of the following would **not** affect the rate of the reaction?

   A   Increasing the volume of the acid

   B   Decreasing the size of the marble chips

   C   Decreasing the concentration of the acid

   D   Increasing the temperature of the acid

4. Which line in the table describes a **neutron**?

	Mass	Charge
A	1	−1
B	negligible	0
C	1	+1
D	1	0

5. An atom has 26 protons, 26 electrons and 30 neutrons. The atom has

   A   atomic number 26, mass number 56

   B   atomic number 56, mass number 30

   C   atomic number 30, mass number 26

   D   atomic number 52, mass number 56.

6. Excess magnesium is burned in an enclosed volume of air.

   Which line in the table best describes the gas after burning is complete?

	Oxygen	Nitrogen	Carbon dioxide
A	1%	98%	0·03%
B	1%	79%	19%
C	16%	79%	4%
D	20%	79%	0·03%

7. Copper is a good conductor of electricity because

   A   the atoms are free to vibrate

   B   the atoms are in close contact

   C   the atoms have the electron arrangement 2, 8, 18, 1

   D   electrons can move readily from one atom to the next.

[Turn over

8. What is the charge on the chromium ion in $CrCl_3$?

   A 1+

   B 1–

   C 3+

   D 3–

9. What name is given to the reaction shown by the following equation?

   $$C_6H_{12}O_6 + 6O_2 \rightarrow 6CO_2 + 6H_2O$$

   A Combustion

   B Condensation

   C Dehydration

   D Hydrolysis

10. The fractional distillation of crude oil depends on the fact that different hydrocarbons have different

    A densities

    B solubilities

    C boiling points

    D ignition temperatures.

11. Which of the following molecules would most likely be present in petrol?

    A CH_4

    B C_3H_8

    C C_8H_{18}

    D $C_{14}H_{30}$

12. Which of the following compounds belongs to the same homologous series as the compound with the molecular formula C_3H_8?

    A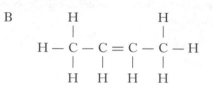

    B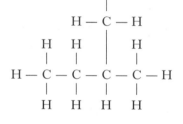

    C

    D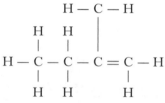

13.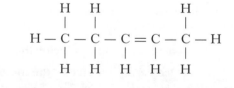

    The name of the above compound is

    A but-2-ene

    B pent-2-ene

    C but-3-ene

    D pent-3-ene.

14. When propene undergoes an addition reaction with hydrogen bromide, two products are formed.

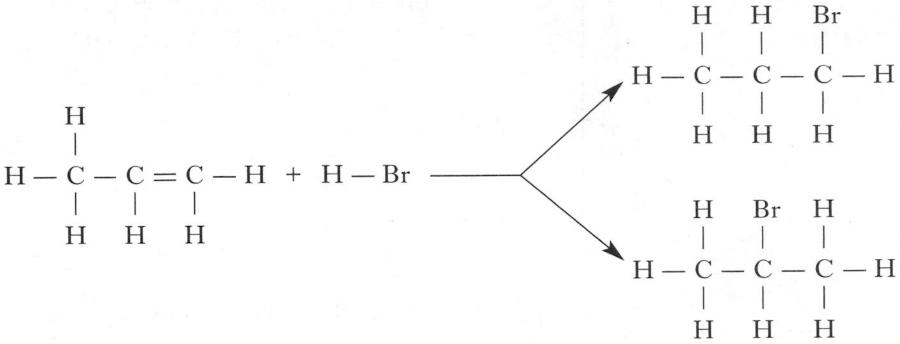

Which of the following alkenes will also produce **two** products when it undergoes an addition reaction with hydrogen bromide?

A Ethene

B But-1-ene

C But-2-ene

D Hex-3-ene

15. The table shows the result of heating two compounds with acidified potassium dichromate solution.

Compound	Acidified potassium dichromate solution
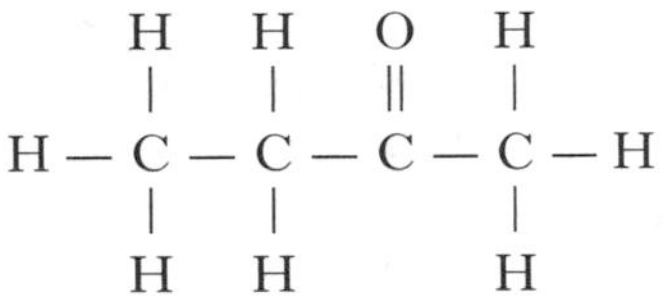	stays orange
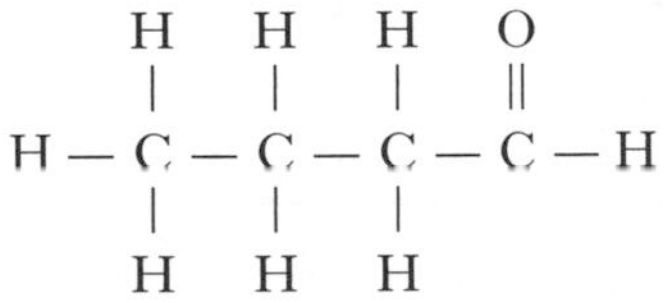	turns green

Which of the following compounds will **not** turn acidified potassium dichromate solution green?

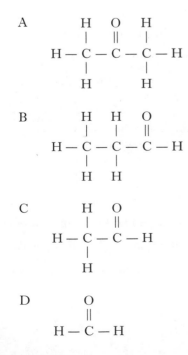

A

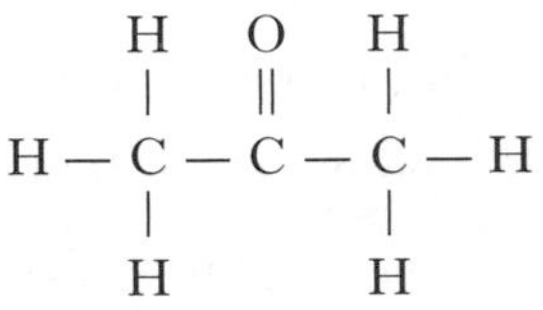

B

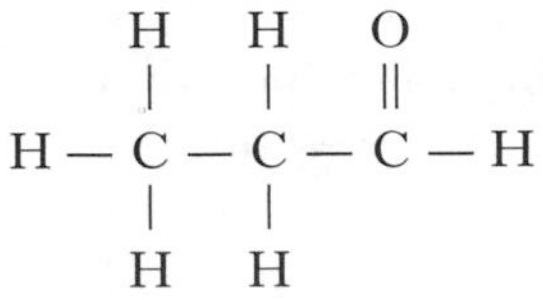

C

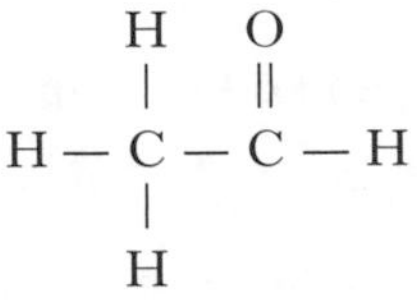

D

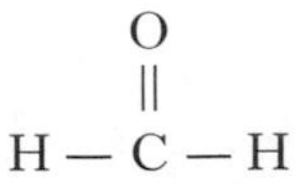

16. $C_6H_{12}O_6$ $C_{12}H_{22}O_{11}$

The above compounds are

A   isomers

B   hydrocarbons

C   alkanols

D   carbohydrates.

17. What functional group is **always** found in a protein molecule?

A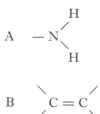

B

C
$$\begin{matrix} & O & H \\ & \| & | \\ -\, & C & -\, N\, - \end{matrix}$$

D
$$\begin{matrix} & O & & \\ & \| & & | \\ -\, & C & -\, O\, -\, C\, - \\ & & & | \end{matrix}$$

18. Which of the following are polymers?

A   Plant sugars

B   Animal fats

C   Marine oils

D   Vegetable proteins

19. Fats and oils are essential in the diet.

Which line in the table best describes an oil?

	Degree of unsaturation	Melting point
A	high	relatively high
B	high	relatively low
C	low	relatively high
D	low	relatively low

20. When one molecule of fat is completely hydrolysed, the number of ester links broken is

A   1

B   2

C   3

D   4.

21. Which of the following oxides dissolves in water to produce a solution with a pH greater than 7?

A Na_2O

B Al_2O_3

C SO_2

D Ag_2O

22. Which line in the table describes what happens to a dilute solution of hydrochloric acid when water is added to it?

	pH	$H^+(aq)$ concentration
A	increases	increases
B	increases	decreases
C	decreases	increases
D	decreases	decreases

23. Which of the following solutions has the highest pH?

A $0 \cdot 1$ mol l^{-1} ammonia

B $0 \cdot 1$ mol l^{-1} hydrochloric acid

C $0 \cdot 1$ mol l^{-1} sodium chloride

D $0 \cdot 1$ mol l^{-1} sodium hydroxide

24. Which of the following pairs of chemicals react to produce a gas that turns lime water milky?

A   Calcium carbonate and dilute hydrochloric acid

B   Copper oxide and dilute sulphuric acid

C   Copper and dilute hydrochloric acid

D   Magnesium and dilute sulphuric acid

25. $H^+(aq) + NO_3^-(aq) + K^+(aq) + OH^-(aq) \longrightarrow K^+(aq) + NO_3^-(aq) + H_2O$

The spectator ions in the reaction are

A $H^+(aq)$ and $K^+(aq)$

B $NO_3^-(aq)$ and $OH^-(aq)$

C $H^+(aq)$ and $OH^-(aq)$

D $K^+(aq)$ and $NO_3^-(aq)$.

26. Which of the following metals would react with zinc chloride solution?

(You may wish to use page 7 of the data booklet to help you.)

A   Copper

B   Gold

C   Iron

D   Magnesium

27.

Metal	Reaction with	
	Dilute acid	Water
X	reacts	no reaction
Y	no reaction	no reaction
Z	reacts	reacts

Which of the following shows the metals in order of **increasing** reactivity?

A   X Y Z

B   Y X Z

C   Z X Y

D   Z Y X

28. Some metals can be obtained from their metal oxides by heat alone.

Which of the following oxides would produce a metal when heated?

A   Calcium oxide

B   Copper oxide

C   Zinc oxide

D   Silver oxide

29. For iron to rust

A   only water must be present

B   only oxygen must be present

C   both water and oxygen must be present

D   oxygen, water and salt must be present.

30. The coatings on four strips of iron were scratched to expose the iron. The strips were placed in salt solution.

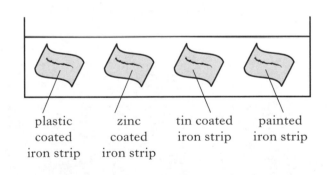

plastic coated iron strip   zinc coated iron strip   tin coated iron strip   painted iron strip

Which iron strip would have rusted most quickly?

A   Plastic coated

B   Zinc coated

C   Tin coated

D   Painted

Candidates are reminded that the answer sheet for Section A MUST be placed INSIDE the front cover of this answer book.

[BLANK PAGE]

DO NOT
WRITE IN
THIS
MARGIN

SECTION B

Marks

50 marks are available in this section of the paper.

All answers must be written clearly and legibly in ink.

1. The properties of a substance depend on its type of bonding and structure.

   There are four types of bonding and structure.

Discrete covalent molecular	Covalent network	Ionic lattice	Metallic lattice

   (*a*) Complete the table to match up each type of bonding and structure with its properties.

Bonding and structure type	Properties
	do not conduct electricity and have high melting points
	have high melting points and conduct electricity when liquid but not when solid
	conduct electricity when solid and have a wide range of melting points
	do not conduct electricity and have low melting points

2

   (*b*) A section of a covalent network compound is shown below.

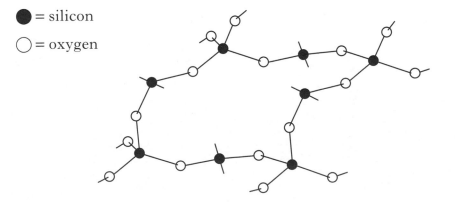

● = silicon

○ = oxygen

   Write the formula for this covalent network compound.

   _____

1

(3)

Marks

2. Information on some two-element molecules is shown in the table.

Name	Formula	Shape of molecule
hydrogen fluoride	HF	○—●
water	H_2O	● with two ○
ammonia	NH_3	

(a) Complete the table to show the **shape** of a molecule of ammonia.   1

(b) The hydrogen fluoride molecule can be represented as:

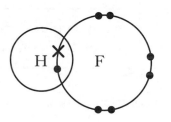

Showing **all** outer electrons, draw a similar diagram to represent a molecule of water, H_2O.

1

(2)

Marks

3. Hydrogen peroxide is a useful bleaching agent and is contained in many hair dyes. Over time, the hair dye becomes less effective as the hydrogen peroxide decomposes forming water and oxygen.

The equation for the decomposition of hydrogen peroxide is:

$$H_2O_2(aq) \longrightarrow O_2(g) + H_2O(\ell)$$

(a) Balance this equation.

1

(b) The above reaction is often used to make oxygen in the laboratory. To speed up the reaction, the catalyst manganese dioxide is added.

Complete the diagram to show how the oxygen can be collected.

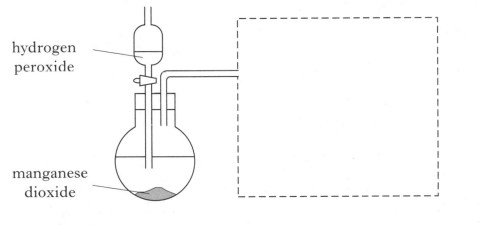

1

(c) State the test for oxygen gas.

_____

1

(d) When 34 g of hydrogen peroxide decomposes, 12 litres of oxygen is produced.

Calculate the volume of oxygen produced when 1·7 g of hydrogen peroxide decomposes.

_____ litres 1

(4)

Marks

4. Research is being carried out into making chemicals that can be used to help relieve the side effects of chemotherapy.

   Part of the process is shown.

   chemical **A** + hydrogen $\xrightarrow{\text{catalyst}}$ chemical **B**

   (a) (i) This reaction is catalysed using the homogeneous catalyst, ruthenium(II) chloride.

      What is meant by a homogeneous catalyst?

      _____

      _____   **1**

      (ii) Write the formula for ruthenium(II) chloride.

      1

   (b) As the reaction proceeds the hydrogen is used up and the pressure decreases.

Time (min)	0	5	10	15	20	30	35	45
Decrease in pressure (bar)	0	0·6	1·2	1·7	2·2	2·9	3·1	3·1

Page twelve

Marks

4. **(b)** **(continued)**

(i) Draw a line graph showing the decrease in pressure as time proceeds.

(Additional graph paper, if required, will be found on *Page twenty-six*.)

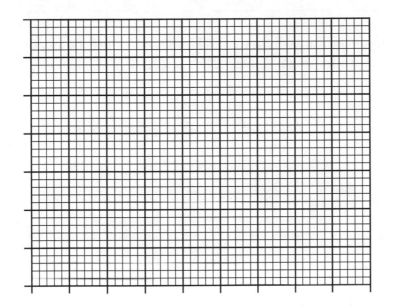

2

(ii) Using your graph, at what time did the reaction finish?

_____ min   1

(iii) Calculate the average rate of the reaction, in bar min^{-1}, between 10 and 20 minutes.

_____ bar min^{-1} 1

(6)

DO NOT WRITE IN THIS MARGIN

Marks

5. Ammonium sulphate is a commonly used fertiliser. It can be produced by the reaction between ammonium carbonate and calcium sulphate.

$$(NH_4)_2CO_3(aq) + CaSO_4(aq) \longrightarrow (NH_4)_2SO_4(aq) + CaCO_3(s)$$

(*a*) Name this type of chemical reaction.

______________________________ **1**

(*b*) What mass of ammonium carbonate, $(NH_4)_2CO_3$, would be needed to make 13·2 kg of ammonium sulphate, $(NH_4)_2SO_4$?

__________ kg **2**

(3)

Marks

6. In the **PPA "Hydrolysis of starch"**, dilute hydrochloric acid can be used to break down starch.

A section of a student's workcard is shown.

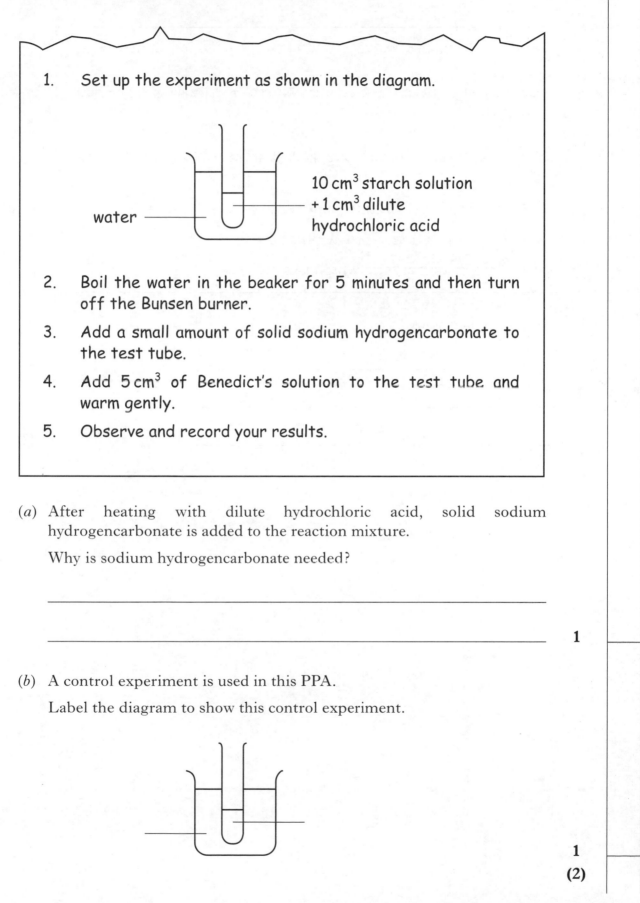

1. Set up the experiment as shown in the diagram.

    water —— 10 cm³ starch solution + 1 cm³ dilute hydrochloric acid

2. Boil the water in the beaker for 5 minutes and then turn off the Bunsen burner.

3. Add a small amount of solid sodium hydrogencarbonate to the test tube.

4. Add 5 cm³ of Benedict's solution to the test tube and warm gently.

5. Observe and record your results.

(*a*) After heating with dilute hydrochloric acid, solid sodium hydrogencarbonate is added to the reaction mixture.

Why is sodium hydrogencarbonate needed?

_____

_____ 1

(*b*) A control experiment is used in this PPA.

Label the diagram to show this control experiment.

1

(2)

DO NOT WRITE IN THIS MARGIN

Marks

7. When marking a student's report on plastics, the teacher circled three errors.

The marked report is shown.

> Most plastics are made from chemicals which come from [1]coal.
> Plastics are made when monomers polymerise to form polymers.
>
> Some common plastics are polystyrene, poly(ethene) and Biopol:
>
> - Polystyrene is made from the monomer [2]propene
> - Poly(ethene) is a thermoplastic
> - [3]Biopol is a plastic which is soluble in water.

Correct the circled errors.

1 ____

2 ____

3 ____ **(3)**

Marks

8. Many different gases are found in car exhaust fumes. Some of these gases are produced by the combustion of petrol in car engines.

The pie chart shows the gases present in the exhaust fumes of a car.

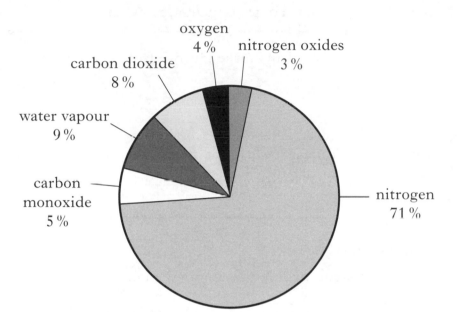

(*a*) What evidence in the pie chart shows that incomplete combustion of petrol has taken place?

_____ 1

(*b*) The car's exhaust fumes were found to contain 3 % nitrogen oxides.

Predict the percentage of nitrogen oxides that could be found in the exhaust fumes if the car was fitted with a catalytic convertor.

_____ % 1

(*c*) The burning of some fuels releases sulphur dioxide into the atmosphere.

Why is this a problem?

_____

_____ 1

(3)

Marks

9.

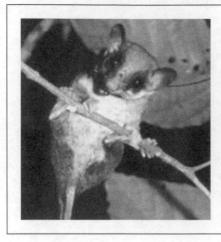 The little pen-tailed tree shrew, found in the jungles of West Malaysia, feeds on nectar from the Bertam palm tree. This nectar contains glucose which ferments, producing solutions of up to 3·8% alcohol. Therefore, the tree shrew regularly drinks a solution which is equivalent to a man drinking 9 units of alcohol per day. It seems that the tree shrew never gets drunk because it is able to breakdown the alcohol much quicker than humans can.

(*a*) Name the process by which plants make glucose from carbon dioxide and water.

_____   1

(*b*) What **type** of substance must be present in the nectar to allow the fermentation of glucose to take place?

_____   1

(*c*) The alcohol produced is ethanol.

Draw the **shortened structural formula** for ethanol.

1

(*d*) Using information in the passage above, calculate the volume of alcohol solution the tree shrew drinks each day.

$$\text{Volume of alcohol solution} = \frac{\text{units of alcohol} \times 1\cdot25}{\%\ \text{of alcohol}}$$

_____ cm^3 **1**

(4)

Marks

10. Synthetic nappies contain hydrogel polymers which attract and absorb water molecules.

(*a*) The following is part of the structure of a hydrogel polymer.

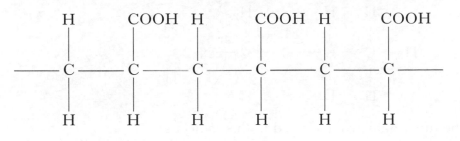

(i) Draw the monomer from which this polymer is made.

1

(ii) The diagram below shows how water molecules are attracted to the hydrogel.

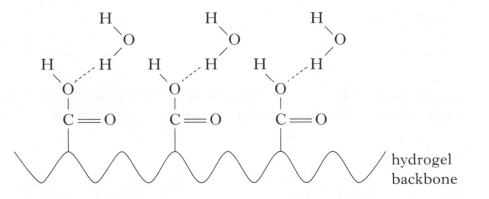

hydrogel backbone

What type of bonding must be present **in the water molecules**, which allows them to be attracted to the hydrogel?

_____ 1

(*b*) Many hydrogels are polymers of carboxylic acids. Carboxylic acids are weak acids.

What is meant by a **weak** acid?

_____

_____ 1

(3)

Marks

11. Many different molecules give us different smells and tastes.

(a) The following molecule gives a "fishy" smell.

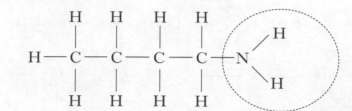

Name the functional group circled in this molecule.

_____   1

(b) Artificial flavourings added to foods are often esters.

The following ester gives an orange flavour.

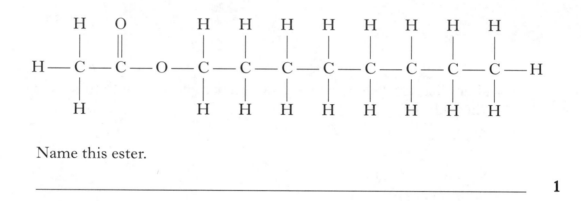

Name this ester.

_____   1

(c) Some household cleaners contain the chemical limonene which gives them a lemon smell. The structure of limonene is shown below.

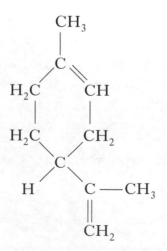

11. *(c)* **(continued)**   *Marks*

Using bromine solution, a student carried out titrations to determine the concentration of limonene in a household cleaner.

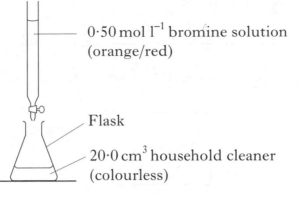

0·50 mol l^{-1} bromine solution
(orange/red)

Flask

20·0 cm^3 household cleaner
(colourless)

Titration	Initial burette reading (cm^3)	Final burette reading (cm^3)	Titre (cm^3)
1	0·5	17·1	16·6
2	0·2	16·3	16·1
3	0·1	16·0	15·9

(i) What colour change would be seen in the flask that indicates the end point of the titrations?

_____   to   _____   **1**

(ii) What average volume should be used in calculating the concentration of limonene?

_____ cm^3 **1**

(iii) The equation for the reaction between limonene and bromine solution is shown.

$$C_{10}H_{16}(aq) + 2Br_2(aq) \longrightarrow C_{10}H_{16}Br_4(aq)$$

0·0 4

Calculate the concentration of limonene in the household cleaner.

_____ mol l^{-1} **2**

(6)

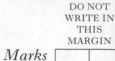

Marks

12. Metals can be extracted from metal compounds by heat alone, heating with carbon or by electrolysis.

(*a*) Name the type of chemical reaction which takes place when a metal is extracted from its compound.

_____   1

(*b*) In a **PPA**, a solution of copper(II) chloride was electrolysed.

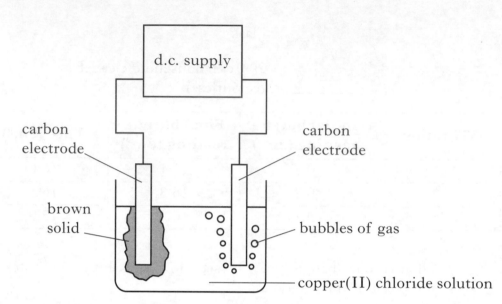

(i) Complete the table by adding the charge for each electrode.

Observation at _____ electrode	Observation at _____ electrode
bubbles of gas	brown solid formed

1

(ii) How could the gas be identified?

_____

_____   1

(3)

DO NOT WRITE IN THIS MARGIN

Marks

13. Some indicators can have different colours when in solutions of different pH values.

The tables give information about two indicators, bromothymol blue and methyl orange.

Bromothymol blue	
Colour	**pH**
yellow	below 6·0
blue	above 7·6

Methyl orange	
Colour	**pH**
red	below 3·1
yellow	above 4·4

The pH of three solutions was investigated using both indicators.

The results are shown below.

Substance	**Colour with bromothymol blue**	**Colour with methyl orange**
A	yellow	red
B	yellow	yellow
C	blue	yellow

(*a*) Which solution is alkaline?

Solution ______________ **1**

(*b*) Suggest a pH value for solution B.

pH ______________ **1**

(2)

[Turn over

Marks

14. The voltage obtained when different pairs of metal strips are connected in a cell varies and this leads to the electrochemical series.

Using the apparatus below, a student investigated the electrochemical series. Copper and four other metal strips were used in this investigation.

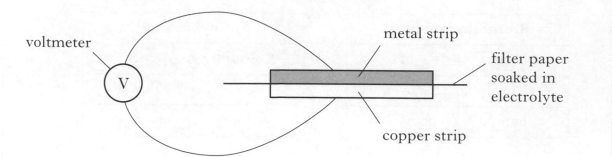

The results are shown.

Metal strip	Voltage (V)	Direction of electron flow
1	0·6	metal 1 to copper
2	0·2	copper to metal 2
3	0·9	metal 3 to copper
4	0·1	copper to metal 4

(a) Which of the metals used is highest in the electrochemical series?

metal _____   1

(b) Which **two** of the metals used would produce the highest voltage when connected in a cell?

metal _____ and metal _____   1

(c) What would be the reading on the voltmeter if both strips of metal were copper?

_____ V   1

(d) Why can glucose solution **not** be used as the electrolyte?

_____ 1

(4)

Marks

15. Fizzy drinks contain acids.

These acids can attack the compound calcium hydroxyapatite which is found in tooth enamel.

The equation for the reaction is:

$$Ca_{10}(PO_4)_6(OH)_2(s) + 8H^+(aq) \longrightarrow 6CaHPO_4(s) + 4Ca^{2+}(aq) + 2 H_2O(\ell)$$

calcium hydroxyapatite

(a) What will happen to the pH as the tooth enamel is attacked by the acids?

_____   1

(b) Fluoride prevents tooth decay by replacing the hydroxide ions of calcium hydroxyapatite with fluoride ions to form hard wearing calcium fluoroapatite.

calcium hydroxyapatite $\xrightarrow{\text{fluoride ions}}$ calcium fluoroapatite
$Ca_{10}(PO_4)_6(OH)_2$

Write the formula for calcium fluoroapatite.

1
(2)

[END OF QUESTION PAPER]

ADDITIONAL SPACE FOR ANSWERS

ADDITIONAL GRAPH PAPER FOR QUESTION 4(b)(i)

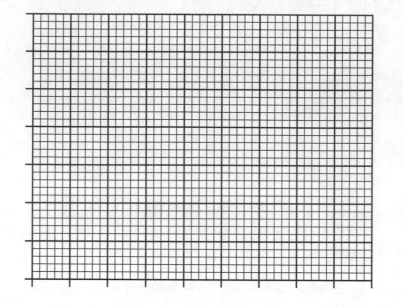

ADDITIONAL SPACE FOR ANSWERS

DO NOT
WRITE IN
THIS
MARGIN

Acknowledgements

Permission has been sought from all relevant copyright holders and Bright Red Publishing is grateful for the use of the following:

Extract adapted from 'The Acid Test' by Robert I Wolke, taken from The Washington Post 10 November 2004 © Robert I Wolke (2008 page 18).

An extract adapted from 'Autumn days' by Victoria Ashton. Taken from 'Education in Chemistry', Vol 38, No 5, September 2001 © Royal Society of Chemistry (2010 page 18).

INTERMEDIATE 2 | ANSWER SECTION

CHEMISTRY INTERMEDIATE 2
2007

SECTION A

1. B	2. D	3. A
4. D	5. C	6. A
7. B	8. B	9. D
10. D	11. A	12. B
13. C	14. B	15. D
16. C	17. B	18. B
19. D	20. A	21. B
22. C	23. C	24. D
25. A	26. B	27. C
28. B	29. A	30. D

SECTION B

1. (a)

In the nucleus		
Name of particle	Relative mass	Charge
Proton	1	+1
Neutron	1	0

Outside the nucleus		
Name of particle	Relative mass	Charge
Electron	almost zero	-/negative

  (b) (i) 2

     (ii) X

2. (a) 1·45

  (b) (i) Reactant and catalyst are in the same state.

     (ii) amber/would be the same

3. (a) delocalised (free) electrons/electrons are free to move/electrons can pass through

  (b) (i) Neutralisation

     (ii) (Polar) Covalent

4. (a) (i) (aq)

     (ii) (Burning splint) burns with a pop/squeak

  (b) 1 mole $\longrightarrow$ 1 mole

    24·3 g $\longrightarrow$ 2 g

    4·9 g $\longrightarrow$ 4·9/24·3 x 2

              = 0·4 g

5. (a)

H–C–C–S–H **or** H–C–C–SH (with H H / H H groups as shown)

  (b) 2-methylpropane-1-thiol/2methylpropane-1-thiol/ 2methylpropane 1 thiol

  (c) Sulphur dioxide/SO_2

6. (a)

Hydrocarbon	Molecular formula	Observation with bromine solution	Saturated or unsaturated
A	C_6H_{14}	no change	saturated
B	C_6H_{12}	bromine decolorises	unsaturated
C	C_6H_{12}	no change	saturated
D	C_6H_{10}	bromine decolorises	unsaturated

  (b) Using safety gloves./ Washing off any spills with sodium thiosulphate.

  (c) Hexene or any isomer of hexene with double bond

7. (a) Carbon to carbon double bond/double bond

  (b)

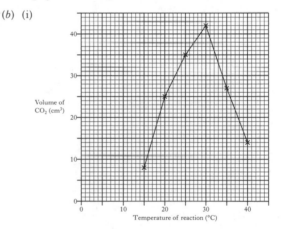

  (c) poly(phenylethene)/polyphenylethene

8. (a) $2C_2H_5OH + 2CO_2$

  (b) (i)

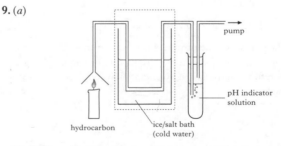

     (ii) Enzyme has been denatured/ destroyed/changes shape./Enzyme can't function/doesn't work.

9. (a)

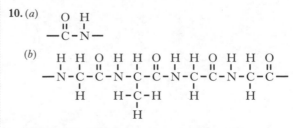

  (b) Carbon dioxide dissolves to form an acid solution./In solution carbon dioxide is acidic.

10. (a)

O H
‖ |
–C–N–

  (b)

–N–C–C–N–C–C–N–C–C–N–C–C– (condensation polymer chain as shown)

  (c) Condensation

11. (a) Iron loses electrons to the copper./ Electrons 'flow' from iron to copper./ Iron gives sacrificial protection to copper.

    (b) Seawater contains ions (which act as an electrolyte)./It is a better electrolyte/contains more ions.

    (c) Fe_2O_3 or $(Fe^{3+})_2(O^{2-})_3$

12. (a) Electrode A/Positive electrode

    (b) $2Na^+ + 2H^+ \rightarrow 2Na + H_2$

    (c) higher

    higher

13. (a) (i) 2, 0

    (ii) Lithium atoms are too/very reactive./Lithium ions are more stable/less reactive.

    (b) The further the metals are from copper, the greater the voltage/The higher in the ECS the metal is, the greater the voltage/The more reactive the higher the voltage.

14. (a)

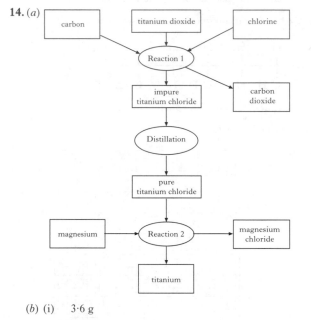

    (b) (i) 3·6 g

    (ii) 0·075

15. (a) sulphuric acid/H_2SO_4

    (b) (i) To remove any unreacted magnesium/To remove any solid (residue) which is left over/To make sure no solid is left over.

    (ii) Evaporation/boil off water

    (c) The energy of the products is less than that of the reactants/Energy decreases from reactants to products, therefore energy is lost/Reactants have higher chemical energy.

CHEMISTRY INTERMEDIATE 2
2008

SECTION A

1. B	2. C	3. C
4. D	5. D	6. A
7. A	8. D	9. A
10. C	11. D	12. C
13. D	14. C	15. B
16. A	17. C	18. D
19. A	20. C	21. B
22. C	23. B	24. A
25. A	26. D	27. D
28. D	29. C	30. D

SECTION B

1. (a) Transition (metal)

    (b) (i)

	Number of protons	Number of neutrons
$^{63}_{29}Cu$	29	34
$^{65}_{29}Cu$	29	36

    (ii) isotopes

2. (a) 46g

    (b) (i) 46-37 = 9 g

    (ii) Filtration/filter/filtering

3. (a) $4N_2O + CH_4 \rightarrow 4N_2 + CO_2 + 2H_2O$ (or multiples of)

    (b) Different (physical) state/form from reactants

    (c) Products released/move/leave from catalyst surface

    (d) *Either:* Sulphur poisons the catalyst

    or Sulphur blocks the active sites

    or Sulphur prevents reactants from binding/adsorbing

4. (a) Breakdown of a compound/solution (to its elements) by passing electricity through it.

    (b) *Any one from:*

    • Allows the products to be identified
    • To make sure the products are produced at only one electrode
    • Direction of electrons stays the same

    • Electrodes keep the same charge

    (c) (i) *Bubbles of gas-* Positive
       Brown solid formed- Negative

    (ii) By carefully smelling the gas/Smells like a swimming pool/Wafting the gas carefully to your nose
       or (Bleaches) blue litmus paper

5. (a) Tetrahedral/Tetrahedron

    (b) (i)

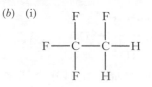

or

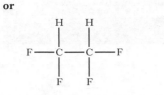

or CF_3CH_2F **or** CHF_2CHF_2

(ii) Chlorine/Cl/Cl_2

(iii) Shorter atmospheric life/biodegrades faster

6. (a) hydroxyl

(b)

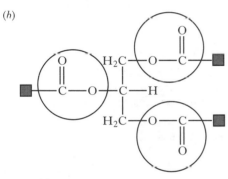

(c) *Any one from:*
- Soluble in water/dissolves
- Breaks down in water
- Degrades in water
- Disintegrates in water

7. (a) *Any one from:*
- Man-made/made by chemists/scientists/man
- Does not occur naturally
- Not natural

(h)

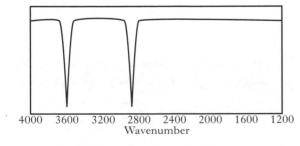

(c) Glycerol/glycerine
   or Propan-1,2,3-triol

8. (a) Carbon-carbon double bond
   or C=C
   or Double covalent bond

(b) Absorption at 2800–3000 and at 3600

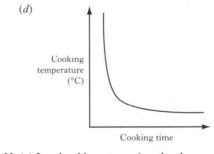

9. (a) Glucose/$C_6H_{12}O_6$

(b) Iodine/I/I_2

(c) (i)

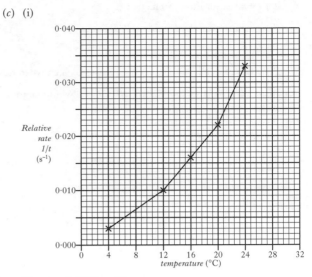

(ii) $1 \div 0.0125 = 80$ secs

10. (a) *Any one from:*
- Protein molecules become unravelled
- The bonds holding the protein molecules are broken
- Shape of the molecule is changed
- Specific shape is changed
- Destroyed

(b) Using an acid/marinating in lime juice/ marinating in citric acid

(c) *Any one from:*
- Bonds are weak
- Bonds are not strong
- Polar bonds are weak
- Hydrogen bonds are weak

(d)

Cooking temperature (°C)

Cooking time

11. (a)
2 moles Al	→	6 moles Ag
54 g	→	648 g
1 g	→	648 ÷ 54 g
0·135 g	→	648 ÷ 54 × 0·135 g
		= 1·62 g

(b) Measure mass of beaker at start and again at the end. (Should have decreased.)
Find mass difference

12. (a) Carbon dioxide (CO_2)

(b) $C_6H_8O_7$

(c) weak

13. (a) Precipitation

(b) Nitric (acid)/hydrogen nitrate/HNO_3

(c) Red

14. (a) *Any one from:*
- Completes the circuit
- Allows ions to move
- To allow electricity to flow freely
- Carry current

(b) (i) Oxidation/loss of electrons

(ii) Aluminium hydroxide/Al(OH)$_3$

15. (a) KMnO$_4$

(b) Provides reaction with oxygen/Releases oxygen when heated

(c) Reaction would be too vigorous/Reaction would be too violent

CHEMISTRY INTERMEDIATE 2 2009

SECTION A

1.	A	11.	A	21.	D
2.	C	12.	B	22.	B
3.	D	13.	C	23.	A
4.	B	14.	D	24.	D
5.	B	15.	C	25.	C
6.	A	16.	A	26.	C
7.	D	17.	D	27.	A
8.	C	18.	A	28.	C
9.	B	19.	D	29.	A
10.	D	20.	A	30.	B

SECTION B

1. (a) 11
   13

   (b) (i)

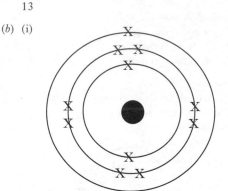

   (ii) The attraction/pull/electrostatic force to the positively charged nucleus (and the (negatively charged) electrons)
   Attraction/pull/electrostatic force between (positive) protons

2. (a) Potassium permanganate
   Water
   (Conc.) Sulphuric acid

   (b) (i) As the atomic number increases the melting point increases

   (ii) 470°C ± 20

3. (a) Exothermic

   (b) (i) Both labels + units
   Both scales
   Plotting points
   Joining points

   (ii) 13 g

   (c) Reduces heat loss from beaker to the surroundings

4. (a) Fe$_2$O$_3$ (s) + $\underline{3}$CO(g) ⟶ $\underline{2}$Fe (l) + $\underline{3}$ CO$_2$ (g)

   (b) CO$_2$ (g) + C (s) ⟶ 2 CO (g)
   1 mole ⟶ 2 moles
   12 g ⟶ 56 g
   1200 kg ⟶ 5600 kg

   (c) To provide oxygen (for the reaction which takes place in zone 1)
   To make CO$_2$
   For complete combustion

5. (a) (As gases have) different boiling points
   Different boiling or melting points

   (b) liquid

   (c) Neutralisation

6. (a) A substance that is burned/combusts to produce energy/heat

  (b) (i) Above zero → 35

    (ii) The smaller the number of carbons in the molecule, the more efficient/useful/better (the fuel)

7. (a) Aluminium oxide (Al_2O_3)

  (b) (i) Butene/C_4H_8

    (ii) (Bromine solution would) decolourise/change from brown to colourless

8. (a) Ethyne/etyne

  (b) (i)

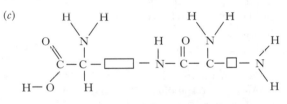

    (ii) Bromines are not attached to adjacent carbon atoms

9. (a)

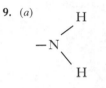

  (b) Amino acids

  (c)

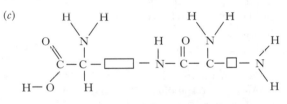

10. (a) Starch + water → glucose

  (b) Fermentation

    Anaerobic respiration

  (c)

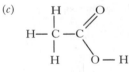

    CH_3COOH

  (d) Methyl ethanoate

11. (a) Biological catalyst

  (b) (i) One which does not completely/partially ionise/dissociate (into ions)

    (ii) Titration
      Volumetric titration

12. (a) 167 (s)

  (b) (Increasing the number of rhubarb cubes) increases the surface area /concentration/ more particles

  (c) (i) $\frac{100}{1000} \times = 0\cdot1$ moles

    (ii) $0\cdot1$ moles reacts with $5/2 \times 0\cdot1 = 0\cdot25$ moles

13. (a) …until no more solid reacts/until it no longer reacts

  (b) To ensure that all of the acid is reacted

  (c) + CO_2 (g) + H_2O (l)

14. (a) Fe_2O_3

  (b) Fe^{2+} (aq) → Fe^{3+} (aq) + e^-

  (c) Iron loses electrons to (less reactive) lead

15. (a) $2OH^-$ (aq) + $2H^+$ (aq) → $2 H_2O$ (l)

  (b) (i) Barium hydroxide solution contains a higher concentration of hydroxide ions

    (ii) There are no free ions in

CHEMISTRY INTERMEDIATE 2 2010

SECTION A

1.	A	11.	A	21.	C
2.	D	12.	D	22.	D
3.	C	13.	B	23.	A
4.	D	14.	D	24.	A
5.	C	15.	B	25.	C
6.	D	16.	C	26.	A
7.	B	17.	A	27.	B
8.	B	18.	A	28.	A
9.	C	19.	B	29.	D
10.	A	20.	C	30.	C

SECTION B

1. (a) Nucleus/nuclei

   (b) (i) 8
      (ii) Same/equal number of (positive) protons as (negative) electrons

         or

         Positive charge of protons cancels negative charge of electrons

         or

         Protons cancel out electrons
      (iii) Alkali metals

2. (a) Endothermic

   (b) *All three required:*
      (s) and (1) and (aq)

   (c) Solvent

   (d) $\dfrac{6\cdot72}{0\cdot2 \times 4\cdot2}$

      $= 8$

3. (a) Covalent (½ mark)
      Network (½ mark)

   (b) (i)

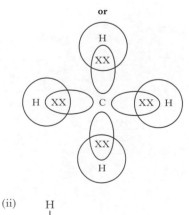

      or

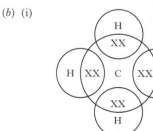

      (ii)

4. (a) (i) 25(%)
      (ii) $25/100 \times 6 = 1\cdot5$

   (b) 4 moles to 2 moles
      $4 \times 108g = 2 \times 248$
      $432 = 496$
      $1\cdot08 = 1\cdot08 \times 496/432$
      $= 1\cdot24$

      or

      no of moles of Ag $= 1\cdot08/108$
                        $= 0\cdot01$ moles
      no of moles of $Ag_2S = 0\cdot01/2$
                        $= 0\cdot005$
      GFM Ag_2S $= 248$
      Mass of $Ag_2S = 0\cdot005 \times 248$
                        $= 1\cdot24$

5. (a) Heat the catalyst first and then the liquid paraffin/ mineral wool

   (b) To prevent suck-back

   (c) (i) Aluminium oxide/Al_2O_3/(Aluminium) silicate
      (ii) Allows reaction to occur at lower temperature/
         Lower energy required/
         Lower activation energy

   (d) Addition

6. (a)

   H H O H H H
   | | ‖ | | |
   H—C—C—C—C—C—C—H
   | | | | |
   H H H H H

   (b) Heptan-4-one

   (c) 147 – 155

7. (a) (i) Fermentation/
         Anaerobic respiration
      (ii) Enzyme/biological catalyst

   (b) Yeast is denatured/destroyed/loses its shape
      Enzyme is denatured/destroyed/loses its shape

   (c) Distillation
      Correct description of the distillation process should include both boiling and condensation stages

8. (a) Esters

   (b) (i) Hydrolysis
      (ii)

      H H H O
      | | | ‖
      H—C—C—C—C
      | | | \
      H H H OH

9. (a) Photosynthesis

   (b) Glucose turns Benedict's (solution) from blue to (brick) red/yellow/orange/green

      or

      Iodine turns blue/black/purple with starch

   (c) Circle /underline any of the – OH groups

   (d) 2,8

10. (a) Any value below 7

    (b) (i) As the temperature increases the solubility decreases
         or
         As the temperature decreases the solubility increases
      (ii) 1.90-1.94

11. (a) Acid rain/
      Dissolved/absorbed SO_2
      Dissolved/absorbed NO_2/oxides of nitrogen/
      Dissolved/absorbed CO_2
      Dissolved/absorbed soluble non metal oxides

(b) (i) *All three required:*
Calcium, carbon, oxygen
$Ca/C/O/O_2$
(ii) Water/H_2O
or hydrogen/H_2

12. (a) Stops air/oxygen **or** water/moisture
Physical barrier to air/oxygen **or** water/moisture
Stops iron losing electrons to oxygen **and** water

(b) (i) Galvanising
(ii) Zinc sacrifices itself
Zinc is being oxidised
Zinc corrodes (by losing electrons)

The zinc gives away its electrons (to the iron)
Zinc is more reactive
Zinc is higher up in the ECS

13. (a) The reading on the pH probe shows 7/neutral

(b) Moles of acid = C × V
= 0·1 × 0·02
= 0·002

1 mole to 2 moles
moles of NaOH = 0·002 × 2 = 0·004
c = n/v
= 0·004/0·05
= 0·08

or

H × C × V = OH × C × V
2 × 0·1 × 20 = 1 × C × 50
4 = 50C

C = 4/50
= 0·08

or

$\frac{C_A V_A}{C_B V_B} = \frac{b}{a}$

$\frac{0·1 × 20}{C_B × 50} = \frac{1}{2}$

$C_B = \frac{0·1 × 20 × 2}{50}$

$= \frac{4}{50}$

= 0·08

14. (a) (i) *All three required:*
LHS = copper/Cu
Top RHS = Iron/Fe
Bottom RHS = $100cm^3$ $0·1 mol l^{-1}$
(ii) Repeated to allow averages/mean to be calculated

(b) (i) From right to left → arrow should be on wires or very close to it
(ii) (good) conductor of electricity
Contains delocalised electrons

SECTION A

1.	B	11.	C	21.	A
2.	D	12.	C	22.	B
3.	A	13.	B	23.	D
4.	D	14.	B	24.	A
5.	A	15.	A	25.	D
6.	A	16.	D	26.	D
7.	D	17.	C	27.	B
8.	C	18.	D	28.	D
9.	A	19.	B	29.	C
10.	C	20.	C	30.	C

SECTION B

1. (a) 1st – covalent network
2nd – ionic lattice
3rd – metallic lattice
4th – discrete covalent/covalent molecules

(b) SiO_2
O_2Si

2. (a)

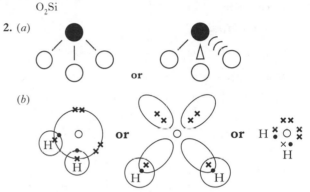

(b)

3. (a) $2H_2O_2(aq) \longrightarrow O_2(g) + 2H_2O(\ell)$

(b) to a syringe/
downward displacement of water into a test-tube or measuring cylinder. Arrangement must work, eg no sealed delivery tubes

(c) relights a glowing splint

(d) 34g ⟶ 12l
1.7g ⟶ 1.7/34 × 12
= 0.6

or

No moles = 1.7/34 = 0.05
Vol = 0.05 x 12
= 0.6

or

34/1.7 = 20, then 12/20
= 0.6

4. (a) (i) (catalyst) in same state/form/physical state as reactants
(ii) $RuC\ell_2$ **or** $Ru^{2+}(C\ell^-)_2$ **or** **or** $Ru_1C\ell_2$

(b) (i)

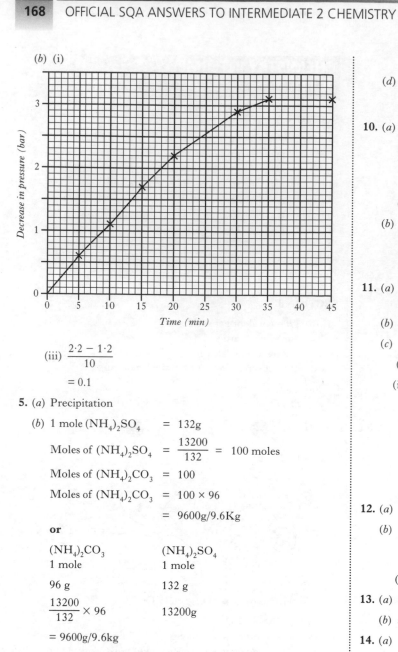

(iii) $\dfrac{2\cdot2 - 1\cdot2}{10}$

$= 0.1$

5. (a) Precipitation

(b) 1 mole $(NH_4)_2SO_4 \quad = 132g$

Moles of $(NH_4)_2SO_4 \quad = \dfrac{13200}{132} = 100$ moles

Moles of $(NH_4)_2CO_3 = 100$

Moles of $(NH_4)_2CO_3 = 100 \times 96$

$= 9600g/9.6Kg$

or

$(NH_4)_2CO_3$	$(NH_4)_2SO_4$
1 mole	1 mole
96 g	132 g
$\dfrac{13200}{132} \times 96$	13200g

$= 9600g/9.6kg$

6. (a) To neutralise the acid, cancel out the acid, use up all/ excess acid

Move pH to 7

(b)

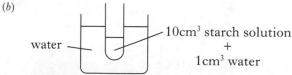

water — 10cm³ starch solution
+
1cm³ water

7. 1. crude oil
   2. styrene
   3. poly(ethenol)/polyethenol

8. (a) Presence of carbon monoxide/
     CO present/
     5% CO present

(b) any value less than 3%

(c) causes acid rain
     Sulphur dioxide reacts and produces/causes acid rain

9. (a) Photosynthesis

(b) Enzyme/
     Biological catalyst

(c) $CH_3-CH_2-OH/CH_3--CH_2OH$
     $CH_3 \, CH_2 \, OH/CH_3CH_2--OH$
     $CH_3 \, CH_2(OH)$

(d) $\dfrac{9 \times 1.25}{3.8}$

$= 2.96$

10. (a) (i)

$$\begin{array}{ccc} H & & COOH \\ | & & | \\ C & = & C \\ | & & | \\ H & & H \end{array}$$

(ii) Polar covalent

(b) It partially ionises/
It partially dissociates
Doesn't dissociate easily
Doesn't fully dissociate

11. (a) amine/
amino

(b) octyl ethanoate

(c) (i) colourless to orange/brown/red/yellow

(ii) 16.0

(iii) moles of $Br_2 = 0.5 \times 0.016$
$\qquad\qquad\qquad = 0.008$

moles of $C_{10}H_{16} = \dfrac{0.008}{2} = 0.004$

concentration of $C_{10}H_{16} = \dfrac{0.004}{0.02}$
$\qquad\qquad\qquad\qquad = 0.2$

12. (a) reduction

(b) (i) $\qquad$ Positive $\qquad$ negative
$\qquad\qquad\qquad$ + $\qquad\qquad$ –
$\qquad\qquad$ (both required for 1 mark)

(ii) Decolourise/bleaching of pH/litmus paper

13. (a) C

(b) any value above 4.4 and below 6.0

14. (a) 3

(b) 2 and 3

(c) 0

(d) it is covalent/glucose is covalent/contains no ions/not ionic

15. (a) (pH) will rise towards 7/
(pH) will rise/
(pH) becomes less acidic/
increases/
becomes neutral

(b) $Ca_{10}(PO_4)_6F_2$